Parrot Fire Kris Northern

"Rather than zoom into the fractal you can zoom into the edge of it and continually find the same pattern repeating itself much like the shoreline of a lake viewed from a plane."– **Kris Northern**

GRADE 5

Prisms and Pyramids

3-D Geometry and Measurement

UNIT 2

Investigations

IN NUMBER, DATA, AND SPACE®

Editorial offices: Glenview, Illinois • Parsippany, New Jersey • New York, New York
Sales offices: Boston, Massachusetts • Duluth, Georgia
Glenview, Illinois • Coppell, Texas • Sacramento, California • Mesa, Arizona

scottforesman.com

The Investigations curriculum was developed by TERC, Cambridge, MA.

This material is based on work supported by the National Science Foundation ("NSF") under Grant No. ESI-0095450. Any opinions, findings, and conclusions or recommendations expressed in this material are those of the author(s) and do not necessarily reflect the views of the National Science Foundation.

ISBN: 0-328-23763-9

ISBN: 978-0-328-23763-0

6 7 8 9 10-V003-15 14 13 12 11 10 09 08
CC:N3

TERC

Co-Principal Investigators

Susan Jo Russell

Karen Economopoulos

Authors

Lucy Wittenberg
Director Grades 3–5

Karen Economopoulos
Director Grades K–2

Virginia Bastable
(SummerMath for Teachers, Mt. Holyoke College)

Katie Hickey Bloomfield

Keith Cochran

Darrell Earnest

Arusha Hollister

Nancy Horowitz

Erin Leidl

Megan Murray

Young Oh

Beth W. Perry

Susan Jo Russell

Deborah Schifter
(Education Development Center)

Kathy Sillman

Administrative Staff

Amy Taber
Project Manager

Beth Bergeron

Lorraine Brooks

Emi Fujiwara

Contributing Authors

Denise Baumann

Jennifer DiBrienza

Hollee Freeman

Paula Hooper

Jan Mokros

Stephen Monk
(University of Washington)

Mary Beth O'Connor

Judy Storeygard

Cornelia Tierney

Elizabeth Van Cleef

Carol Wright

Technology

Jim Hammerman

Classroom Field Work

Amy Appell

Rachel E. Davis

Traci Higgins

Julia Thompson

Note: Unless otherwise noted, all contributors listed above were staff of the Education Research Collaborative at TERC during their work on the curriculum. Other affiliations during the time of development are listed.

Collaborating Teachers

This group of dedicated teachers carried out extensive field testing in their classrooms, met regularly to discuss issues of teaching and learning mathematics, provided feedback to staff, welcomed staff into their classrooms to document students' work, and contributed both suggestions and written material that has been incorporated into the curriculum.

Bethany Altchek
Linda Amaral
Kimberly Beauregard
Barbara Bernard
Nancy Buell
Rose Christiansen
Chris Colbath-Hess
Lisette Colon
Kim Cook
Frances Cooper
Kathleen Drew
Rebeka Eston Salemi
Thomas Fisher
Michael Flynn
Holly Ghazey
Susan Gillis
Danielle Harrington
Elaine Herzog
Francine Hiller
Kirsten Lee Howard
Liliana Klass
Leslie Kramer
Melissa Lee Andrichak
Kelley Lee Sadowski
Jennifer Levitan
Mary Lou LoVecchio
Kristen McEnaney
Maura McGrail
Kathe Millett
Florence Molyneaux
Amy Monkiewicz
Elizabeth Monopoli
Carol Murray
Robyn Musser
Christine Norrman
Deborah O'Brien
Timothy O'Connor
Anne Marie O'Reilly
Mark Paige
Margaret Riddle
Karen Schweitzer
Elisabeth Seyferth
Susan Smith
Debra Sorvillo
Shoshanah Starr
Janice Szymaszek
Karen Tobin
JoAnn Trauschke
Ana Vaisenstein
Yvonne Watson
Michelle Woods
Mary Wright

Advisors

Deborah Lowenberg Ball, University of Michigan

Hyman Bass, Professor of Mathematics and Mathematics Education University of Michigan

Mary Canner, Principal, Natick Public Schools

Thomas Carpenter, Professor of Curriculum and Instruction, University of Wisconsin-Madison

Janis Freckmann, Elementary Mathematics Coordinator, Milwaukee Public Schools

Lynne Godfrey, Mathematics Coach, Cambridge Public Schools

Ginger Hanlon, Instructional Specialist in Mathematics, New York City Public Schools

DeAnn Huinker, Director, Center for Mathematics and Science Education Research, University of Wisconsin-Milwaukee

James Kaput, Professor of Mathematics, University of Massachusetts-Dartmouth

Kate Kline, Associate Professor, Department of Mathematics and Statistics, Western Michigan University

Jim Lewis, Professor of Mathematics, University of Nebraska-Lincoln

William McCallum, Professor of Mathematics, University of Arizona

Harriet Pollatsek, Professor of Mathematics, Mount Holyoke College

Debra Shein-Gerson, Elementary Mathematics Specialist, Weston Public Schools

Gary Shevell, Assistant Principal, New York City Public Schools

Liz Sweeney, Elementary Math Department, Boston Public Schools

Lucy West, Consultant, Metamorphosis: Teaching Learning Communities, Inc.

This revision of the curriculum was built on the work of the many authors who contributed to the first edition (published between 1994 and 1998). We acknowledge the critical contributions of these authors in developing the content and pedagogy of *Investigations*:

Authors

Joan Akers

Michael T. Battista

Douglas H. Clements

Karen Economopoulos

Marlene Kliman

Jan Mokros

Megan Murray

Ricardo Nemirovsky

Andee Rubin

Susan Jo Russell

Cornelia Tierney

Contributing Authors

Mary Berle-Carman

Rebecca B. Corwin

Rebeka Eston

Claryce Evans

Anne Goodrow

Cliff Konold

Chris Mainhart

Sue McMillen

Jerrie Moffet

Tracy Noble

Kim O'Neil

Mark Ogonowski

Julie Sarama

Amy Shulman Weinberg

Margie Singer

Virginia Woolley

Tracey Wright

Contents

UNIT 2

Prisms and Pyramids

INTRODUCTION AND OVERVIEW

INVESTIGATION 1

Finding the Volume of Boxes

INVESTIGATION 2

Using Standard Cubic Units

INVESTIGATION 3

Volume Relationships Among Solids

Investigations

C U R R I C U L U M

Overview of Program Components

FOR TEACHERS

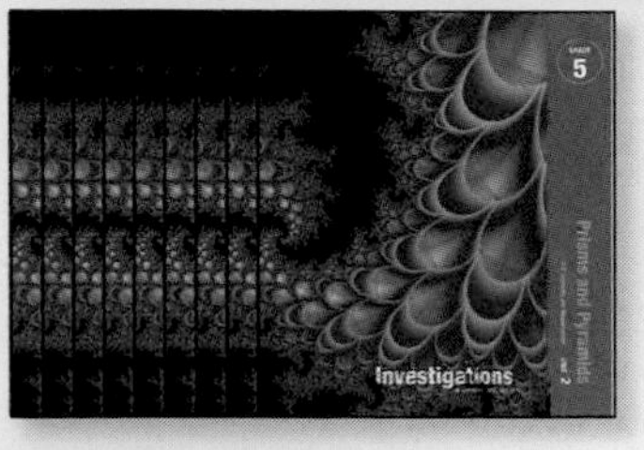

The **Curriculum Units** are the teaching guides. (See far right.)

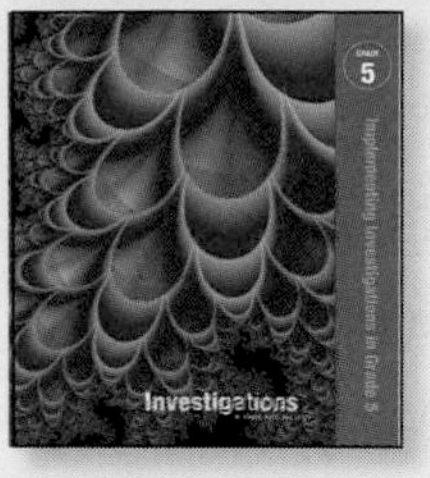

Implementing Investigations in Grade 5 offers suggestions for implementing the curriculum. It also contains a comprehensive index.

The **Resources Binder** contains all the Resource Masters and Transparencies that support instruction. (Also available on CD.) The binder also includes a student software CD.

FOR STUDENTS

The **Student Activity Book** contains the consumable student pages (Recording Sheets, Homework, Practice, and so on).

The **Student Math Handbook** contains Math Words and Ideas pages and Games directions.

The *Investigations* Curriculum

Investigations in Number, Data, and Space® is a K–5 mathematics curriculum designed to engage students in making sense of mathematical ideas. Six major goals guided the development of the *Investigations in Number, Data, and Space®* curriculum. The curriculum is designed to:

- Support students to make sense of mathematics and learn that they can be mathematical thinkers
- Focus on computational fluency with whole numbers as a major goal of the elementary grades
- Provide substantive work in important areas of mathematics—rational numbers, geometry, measurement, data, and early algebra—and connections among them
- Emphasize reasoning about mathematical ideas
- Communicate mathematics content and pedagogy to teachers
- Engage the range of learners in understanding mathematics

Underlying these goals are three guiding principles that are touchstones for the *Investigations* team as we approach both students and teachers as agents of their own learning:

1. *Students have mathematical ideas.* Students come to school with ideas about numbers, shapes, measurements, patterns, and data. If given the opportunity to learn in an environment that stresses making sense of mathematics, students build on the ideas they already have and learn about new mathematics they have never encountered. Students learn that they are capable of having mathematical ideas, applying what they know to new situations, and thinking and reasoning about unfamiliar problems.

2. *Teachers are engaged in ongoing learning* about mathematics content, pedagogy, and student learning. The curriculum provides material for professional development, to be used by teachers individually or in groups, that supports teachers' continued learning as they use the curriculum over several years. The *Investigations* curriculum materials are designed as much to be a dialogue with teachers as to be a core of content for students.

3. *Teachers collaborate with the students and curriculum materials* to create the curriculum as enacted in the classroom. The only way for a good curriculum to be used well is for teachers to be active participants in implementing it. Teachers use the curriculum to maintain a clear, focused, and coherent agenda for mathematics teaching. At the same time, they observe and listen carefully to students, try to understand how they are thinking, and make teaching decisions based on these observations.

Investigations is based on experience from research and practice, including field testing that involved documentation of thousands of hours in classrooms, observations of students, input from teachers, and analysis of student work. As a result, the curriculum addresses the learning needs of real students in a wide range of classrooms and communities. The investigations are carefully designed to invite all students into mathematics—girls and boys; members of diverse cultural, ethnic, and language groups; and students with a wide variety of strengths, needs, and interests.

Based on this extensive classroom testing, the curriculum takes seriously the time students need to develop a strong conceptual foundation and skills based on that foundation. Each curriculum unit focuses on an area of content in depth, providing time for students to develop and practice ideas across a variety of activities and contexts that build on each other. Daily guidelines for time spent on class sessions, Classroom Routines (K–3), and Ten-Minute Math (3–5) reflect the commitment to devoting adequate time to mathematics in each school day.

About This Curriculum Unit

This **Curriculum Unit** is one of nine teaching guides in Grade 5. The second unit in Grade 5 is *Prisms and Pyramids.*

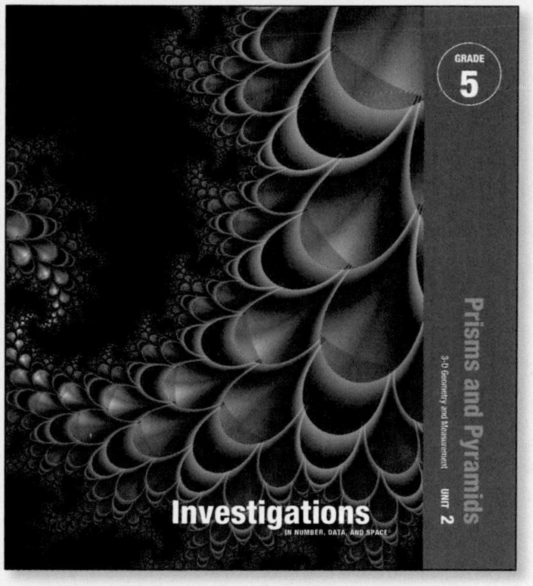

- The **Introduction and Overview** section organizes and presents the instructional materials, provides background information, and highlights important features specific to this unit.
- Each Curriculum Unit contains several **Investigations.** Each Investigation focuses on a set of related mathematical ideas.
- Investigations are divided into one-hour **Sessions,** or lessons.
- Sessions have a combination of these parts: **Activity, Discussion, Math Workshop, Assessment Activity,** and **Session Follow-Up.**
- Each session also has one or more **Ten-Minute Math** activities that are done outside of math time.
- At the back of the book is a collection of **Teacher Notes** and **Dialogue Boxes** that provide professional development related to the unit.
- Also included at the back of the book are the **Student Math Handbook** pages for this unit.
- The **Index** provides a way to look up important words or terms.

Overview

OF THIS UNIT

Investigation	Session	Day
INVESTIGATION 1 **Finding the Volume of Boxes** Students study the volume of rectangular prisms by looking at patterns of boxes and by building rectangular prisms from connecting cubes. They write a strategy for finding the volume of any rectangular prism. They investigate how the dimensions of prisms change when the volume is doubled or halved.	**1.1** How Many Cubes?	1
	1.2 Strategies for Finding Volume	2
	1.3 Doubling the Number of Cubes	3
	1.4 How Many Packages?	4
	1.5 Assessment: Finding the Volume of Rectangular Prisms	5
	1.6 Finding Volume	6
	1.7 Designing Boxes	7
INVESTIGATION 2 **Using Standard Cubic Units** Using standard cubic units of volume, students measure the volume of a small rectangular prism. They build models of cubic inches and feet and of cubic centimeters and meters. Using cubic meters, they measure the space inside their classroom.	**2.1** Finding Cubic Centimeters	8
	2.2 Building Models of Volume Units	9
	2.3 The Space Inside Our Classroom	10
	2.4 Assessment: Measuring Volume in Cubic Centimeters	11
INVESTIGATION 3 **Volume Relationships Among Solids** Students build models of prisms, pyramids, cylinders, and cones. They find the volume of these solids in cubic centimeters. They investigate the relationship between the volume of prisms and pyramids, and the volume of cylinders and cones that have the same base and height.	**3.1** Comparing Volumes	12
	3.2 Finding a Three-to-One Relationship	13
	3.3 Prism and Pyramid Partners	14
	3.4 Using Standard Units of Volume	15
	3.5 End-of-Unit Assessment	16

Each *Investigations* session has some combination of these five parts: **Activity, Discussion, Math Workshop, Assessment Activity,** and **Session Follow-Up.** These session parts are indicated in the chart below. Each session also has one or more **Ten-Minute Math** activities that are done outside of math time.

					Ten-Minute Math	
Activity	Discussion	Math Workshop	Assessment Activity	Session Follow-Up	*Quick Images: 3-D*	*Estimation and Number Sense*
●●●				●	●	
●	●●			●	●	
●	●			●	●	
●●	●			●		●
	●	●	●	●		●
	●	●		●	●	
●	●			●	●	
●	●●			●		●
●●	●			●		●
●	●			●		●
		●		●		●
●●	●			●	●	
●	●			●	●	
●●	●			●		●
●	●			●		●
			●	●		●

Mathematics

IN THIS UNIT

Prisms and Pyramids is the first Grade 5 unit in the Geometry and Measurement strand of *Investigations*. In these units, students develop ideas about the attributes of two-dimensional (2-D) and three-dimensional (3-D) shapes and see how these attributes determine their classification. They also develop ideas about linear measurement (which includes perimeter), area, the measurement of angles, and volume.

LOOKING BACK

In Grade 3, students examined and built models of polyhedra. They developed familiarity with the mathematical vocabulary used to describe prisms and pyramids (face, edge, vertex). They made open boxes and investigated the number of cubes that fit inside the boxes. They began to understand the idea of *volume* and saw how the structure of rectangular prisms can help them determine volume. In Grade 4, students deepened their understanding of the attributes of 3-D figures by describing and naming geometric solids and their components, using the appropriate mathematical terminology. They represented 3-D shapes in 2-D, with a focus on understanding perspective. They also explored how different views of a 3-D object come together to form the whole. Their work with volume focused on analyzing the structure of rectangular prisms constructed from cubes and finding the volume of these prisms.

This unit focuses on 3 Mathematical Emphases:

1 Features of Shape **Translating between two-dimensional and three-dimensional shapes**

Math Focus Points

- Decomposing 3-D shapes and then recombining them to make a given building

Throughout this unit, students continue to develop their visualization skills and their understanding of relationships between 2-D pictures and the 3-D objects they represent. These understandings develop through the Ten-Minute Math activity *Quick Images: 3-D* and as students create and determine the volume of boxes made from 2-D patterns and create box patterns, to hold a given number of cubes.

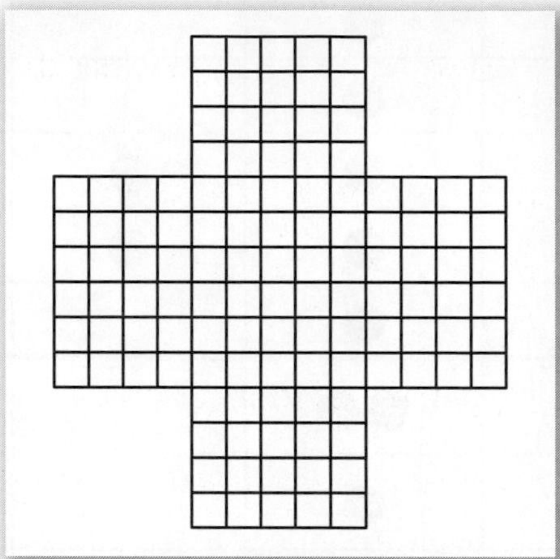

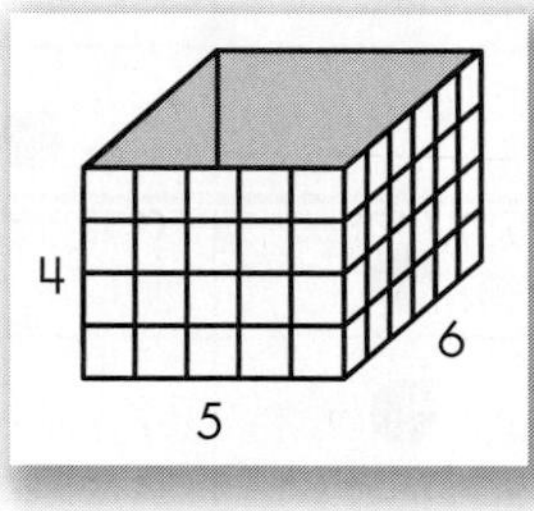

2 Volume Structuring rectangular prisms and determining their volume

Math Focus Points

- Determining the number of cubes that will fit into the box made by a given pattern
- Developing a strategy for determining the volume of rectangular prisms
- Designing patterns for boxes that hold a given number of cubes
- Finding the volume of rectangular prisms
- Considering how the dimensions of a box change when the volume is changed (doubled, halved, or tripled)
- Organizing rectangular packages to fit in rectangular boxes
- Designing a box that can be completely filled with several differently shaped rectangular packages
- Determining the volume, in cubic centimeters, of a small prism
- Constructing units of volume—cubic centimeter, cubic inch, cubic foot, cubic yard (optional), cubic meter
- Choosing an appropriate unit of volume to measure a large space
- Finding the volume of a large space, such as the classroom, using cubic meters

Volume is an essential concept in students' learning of 3-D geometry. Through work in this and previous 3-D units, students come to see that the volume of a solid is the space that the solid occupies. To understand the measurement of volume and why it is measured in cubic units, students first develop strategies for determining the number of cubes in 3-D arrays. They do this by mentally organizing the cubes—for example, as a stack of three rectangular layers, each 3 x 4 cubes.

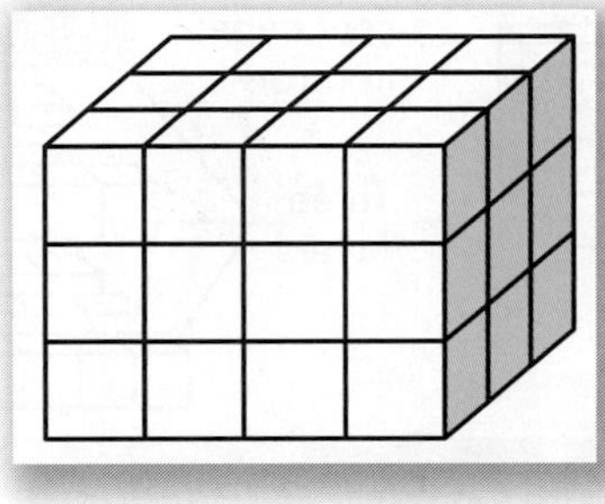

Investigation 1 includes a set of activities designed to help students develop their understanding of the volume of rectangular prisms. They learn the structure of the rectangular boxes they are trying to measure, as well as the structure of the cube arrays that fit inside. As they work through the investigation, most students determine volume by thinking about the number of cubes in rectangular layers: "A layer contains 3 x 4, or 12, cubes, and there are three layers, so there are 36 cubes altogether." By designing boxes for packages that are larger than one cube and boxes that hold double or half the number of cubes as a given box, students deepen their understanding of the relationship between volume and the dimensions of length, width, and height.

This work and the layering strategies that students develop model volume in a powerful and generalizable way. This work also provides an excellent foundation for developing meaningful understanding and application of the formula for volume of rectangular prisms: "volume = length × width × height" or "volume = area of the base × height."

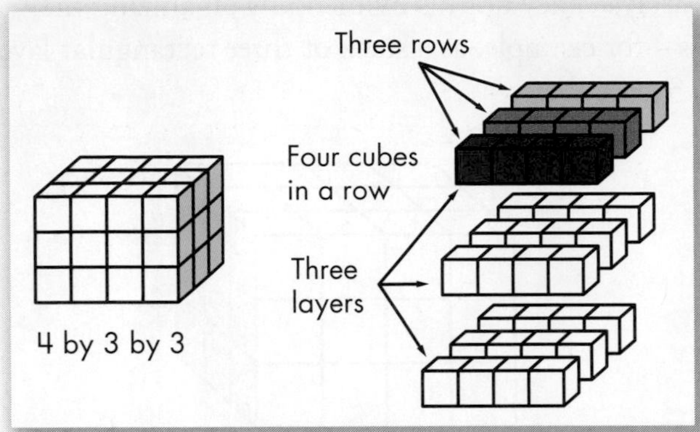

In Investigation 2, students develop an understanding that measuring the dimensions of a box in linear units indicates the number of cubic units that fit along the edges of the box. They apply this understanding and the strategies they developed for finding the volume of rectangular prisms to the task of measuring the volume of a large space—their classroom. Before measuring this space, they build and compare standard units of volume (cubic centimeters, cubic inches, cubic feet, cubic yards [optional], and cubic meters) and they relate linear measurements to the length of the edges of these volume units. They consider the questions of why larger units are more efficient for measuring a large space and why the number reported for volume will vary with the size of the unit. They measure the volume of the classroom in cubic meters and compare their results.

3 Volume **Structuring prisms, pyramids, cylinders, and cones and determining their volume**

Math Focus Points

- Comparing volumes of different-shaped containers
- Finding volume relationships between solids, particularly those with the same base and height
- Building a prism with three times the volume of a given pyramid
- Demonstrating the 3:1 relationship between rectangular prisms and pyramids with the same base and height
- Finding volume, in cubic centimeters, of prisms, pyramids, cylinders, and cones

After students have developed viable strategies for finding the volume of rectangular prisms, they extend their understanding of volume to other solids, such as pyramids, cylinders, and cones. In Investigation 3, they find relationships between the volumes of related pyramids and prisms and between the volumes of related cones and cylinders. For example, after noticing the three-to-one relationship of the volume of certain pairs of prisms and pyramids, they determine that the pyramid and prism in each pair has the same base and height. At the end of the investigation, students measure the volume of geometric solids, using cubic centimeters. This work requires them to develop strategies for using standard units of volume to measure nonrectangular solids.

This Unit also focuses on

- Describing and defending measurement methods
- Building rectangular solids

Ten-Minute Math Activities focus on

- Organizing and analyzing visual images
- Developing language and concepts needed to communicate about spatial relationships
- Decomposing images of 3-D shapes and then recombining them to make a given building
- Estimating solutions to 2- and 3-digit multiplication and division problems
- Breaking apart, reordering, or changing numbers mentally to determine a reasonable estimate

LOOKING FORWARD

In future years, students continue to develop their understanding of the relationship between the linear measurements used to determine the dimensions of a solid and the volume of that solid. Students' ideas about volume from this unit include the strategies they develop for determining the volume of rectangular prisms and their examination of the volume of related solids. These ideas serve as building blocks for understanding formulas for calculating the volume of a variety of shapes.

Technology Note

Getting Started with the *LogoPaths* Software Students are formally introduced to the *LogoPaths* software in the 2-D Geometry and Measurement unit *Measuring Polygons,* the fifth unit in the Grade 5 sequence. However, if you plan to use the software this year, we recommend that students have access to the software **outside of math time** starting with this unit in order to return to *Feed the Turtle,* a *LogoPaths* activity from Grade 3, and to spend time with the *Free Explore* option. For information about the *LogoPaths* software and directions for *Feed the Turtle,* refer to the *Software Support Reference Guide* found on the CD. See **Part 5: Technology in *Investigations:* Calculators and Computers** in *Implementing Investigations in Grade 5:* Introducing and Managing the *LogoPaths* software in Grade 5.

Assessment

IN THIS UNIT

ONGOING ASSESSMENT: Observing Students at Work

The following sessions provide **Ongoing Assessment: Observing Students at Work** opportunities:

- **Session 1.1, p. 29**
- **Session 1.2, p. 33**
- **Session 1.3, p. 38**
- **Session 1.4, p. 45**
- **Session 1.5, pp. 50 and 51**
- **Session 1.7, p. 59**
- **Session 2.1, p. 66**
- **Session 2.2, pp. 73 and 76**
- **Session 2.3, p. 79**
- **Session 2.4, pp. 84 and 86**
- **Session 3.1, pp. 91 and 94**
- **Session 3.2, p. 97**
- **Session 3.3, pp. 101 and 103**
- **Session 3.4, p. 108**
- **Session 3.5, p. 111**

WRITING OPPORTUNITIES

The following sessions have **writing** opportunities for students to explain their mathematical thinking:

- **Session 1.1, p. 29**
  Student Activity Book, p. 3
- **Session 1.3, p. 37**
  Student Activity Book, p. 11
- **Session 1.5, pp. 50–51**
  Student Activity Book, pp. 20–21
- **Session 3.3, p. 104**
  Student Activity Book, p. 45

PORTFOLIO OPPORTUNITIES

The following sessions have work appropriate for a **portfolio**:

- **Session 1.5, p. 49**
  Student Activity Book, p. 19
- **Session 1.5, p. 52**
  M19–M20, Assessment: Finding the Volume of Rectangular Prisms
- **Session 2.4, p. 85**
  M24, Assessment: Measuring Volume in Cubic Centimeters
- **Session 3.5, p. 111**
  M35–M36, End-of-Unit Assessment

Assessing the Benchmarks

Observing students as they engage in conversation about their ideas is a primary means to assess their mathematical understanding. Consider all of your students' work, not just the written assessments. See the chart below for suggestions about key activities to observe.

Checklist Available

Benchmarks in This Unit	Key Activities to Observe	Assessment
1. Find the volume of rectangular prisms.	**Session 1.2:** Strategies for Finding Volume **Sessions 1.5 and 1.6:** Finding the Volume of Boxes	**Session 1.5 Assessment Activity:** Finding the Volume of Rectangular Prisms
2. Use standard units to measure volume.	**Session 2.1:** Finding Cubic Centimeters **Session 2.3:** How Many Cubic Meters in Our Classroom?	**Session 2.4 Assessment Activity:** Measuring Volume in Cubic Centimeters
3. Identify how the dimensions of a box change when the volume is changed.	**Session 1.3:** Doubling the Cubes **Sessions 1.5 and 1.6:** Doubling and Halving	**Session 3.5 Assessment Activity:** End-of-Unit Assessment (Problem 1)
4. Explain the relationship between the volumes of prisms and pyramids with the same base and height.	**Session 3.3:** Designing a Prism	**Session 3.5 Assessment Activity:** End-of-Unit Assessment (Problem 2)

Relating the Mathematical Emphases to the Benchmarks

Mathematical Emphases	Benchmarks
Features of Shape Translating between 2-D and 3-D shapes	1
Volume Structuring rectangular prisms and determining their volume	1, 2, and 3
Volume Structuring prisms, pyramids, cylinders, and cones and determining their volume	4

Ten-Minute Math

IN THIS UNIT

Ten-Minute Math offers practice and review of key concepts for this grade level. These daily activities, to be done in ten minutes outside of math class, are introduced in a unit and repeated throughout the grade. Specific directions for the day's activity are provided in each session. For the full description and variations of each classroom activity, see *Implementing Investigations in Grade 5.*

Activity	Introduced	Full Description of Activity and Its Variations
Quick Images: 3-D	Unit 2, Session 1.1	*Implementing Investigations in Grade 5*
Estimation and Number Sense	Unit 2, Session 1.4	*Implementing Investigations in Grade 5*

Quick Images: 3-D

Students visualize and analyze images of 3-D geometric figures. After briefly viewing an image of a 3-D structure, students build it from the mental image they formed during the brief viewing.

Math Focus Points

- Organizing and analyzing visual images
- Developing language and concepts needed to communicate about spatial relationships
- Decomposing images of 3-D shapes and then recombining them to make a given structure

Estimation and Number Sense

Students make the closest estimate they can for a problem that is created using Digit Cards and a given multiplication or division template. They explain and discuss their strategies for making good estimates.

Math Focus Points

- Estimating solutions to 2- and 3-digit multiplication and division problems
- Breaking apart, reordering, or changing numbers mentally to determine a reasonable estimate

Practice and Review

IN THIS UNIT

Practice and review play a critical role in the *Investigations* program. The following components and features are available to provide regular reinforcement of key mathematical concepts and procedures.

Books	Features	In This Unit . . .
Curriculum Unit	**Ten-Minute Math** offers practice and review of key concepts for this grade level. These daily activities, to be done in ten minutes outside of math class, are introduced in a unit and repeated throughout the grade. Specific directions for the day's activity are provided in each session. For the full description and variations of each classroom activity, see *Implementing Investigations in Grade 5*.	• **All sessions**
Student Activity Book	**Daily Practice** pages in the *Student Activity Book* provide one of three types of written practice: **reinforcement** of the content of the unit, **ongoing review,** or **enrichment** opportunities. Some Daily Practice pages will also have Ongoing Review items with multiple-choice problems similar to those on standardized tests.	• **All sessions**
	Homework pages in the *Student Activity Book* are an extension of the work done in class. At times they help students prepare for upcoming activities.	• **Session 1.1** • **Session 1.2** • **Session 1.3** • **Session 1.4** • **Session 1.6** • **Session 1.7** • **Session 2.1** • **Session 2.2** • **Session 3.1** • **Session 3.3** • **Session 3.4**
Student Math Handbook	**Math Words and Ideas** in the *Student Math Handbook* are pages that summarize key words and ideas. Most Words and Ideas pages have at least one exercise.	• **Student Math Handbook, pp. 105–114**
	Games pages are found in a section of the *Student Math Handbook*.	• **No games are introduced in this unit.**

Supporting the Range of Learners

Sessions	1.1	1.2	1.4	1.5	1.7	2.1	2.2	2.3	2.4	3.3
Intervention	•	•	•	•		•		•		•
Extension	•			•	•				•	•
ELL	•						•			

Intervention

Suggestions are made to support and engage students who are having difficulty with a particular idea, activity, or problem.

Extension

Suggestions are made to support and engage students who finish early or may be ready for additional challenge.

English Language Learners (ELL)

As students work through the material in this unit, they will encounter vocabulary about 3-D shapes and measurement that may be new to them. You can help English Language Learners master this vocabulary by using it in the context of various activities and by providing consistent visual supports. The Math Words and Ideas pages in the *Student Math Handbook* can be a particularly useful reference for the English Language Learners in your classroom. When helpful, students can also create their own word banks to include native language translations or additional vocabulary not included in the Math Words and Ideas pages. Students can add to these word banks throughout the unit. Whenever possible, ask students to review the vocabulary independently or in pairs.

Throughout the unit, students are asked to make comparisons and estimates. You can support English Language Learners by presenting simple situations in which they can hear and practice the relevant language. **Let's compare the length and width of our classroom. If we measure each side of the room, will the measurements be the same or different? Why?** Use visual aids to clarify meaning as much as possible. **Let's estimate how many cubes will fit inside this box. Renaldo, what's your estimate? How did you come up with that number?**

Before some class discussions, you may wish to meet with English Language Learners to preview the questions you plan to ask. By giving these students the chance to formulate answers ahead of time, you can assess their understanding of the math content and provide them with the language support they may require to participate more successfully in these discussions.

Working with the Range of Learners: Classroom Cases is a set of episodes written by teachers that focuses on meeting the needs of the range of learners in the classroom. In the first section, *Setting up the Mathematical Community,* teachers write about how they create a supportive and productive learning environment in their classrooms. In the next section, *Accommodations for Learning,* teachers focus on specific modifications they make to meet the needs of some of their learners. In the last section, *Language and Representation,* teachers share how they help students use representations and develop language to investigate and express mathematical ideas. The questions at the end of each case provide a starting point for your own reflection or for discussion with colleagues. See *Implementing Investigations in Grade 5* for this set of episodes.

INVESTIGATION 1

Mathematical Emphases

Features of Shape Translating between two-dimensional and three-dimensional shapes

Math Focus Points

- Decomposing 3-D shapes and then recombining them to make a given building

Volume Structuring rectangular prisms and determining their volume

Math Focus Points

- Determining the number of cubes that will fit into the box made by a given pattern
- Developing a strategy for determining the volume of rectangular prisms
- Designing patterns for boxes that hold a given number of cubes
- Finding the volume of rectangular prisms
- Considering how the dimensions of a box change when the volume is changed (doubled, halved, or tripled)
- Organizing rectangular packages to fit in rectangular boxes
- Designing a box that can be completely filled with several differently shaped rectangular packages

Finding the Volume of Boxes

SESSION	Student Activity Book	Student Math Handbook	Professional Development: Read Ahead of Time
SESSION 1.1 p. 24 **How Many Cubes?** Students use drawings and written descriptions of rectangular prisms to find the volume of the prism.	1–5	105	• **Mathematics in This Unit,** p. 10 • **Part 4: Ten-Minute Math** in *Implementing Investigations in Grade 5*: *Quick Images: 3-D* and *Estimation and Number Sense* • **Teacher Note:** Strategies for Finding the Number of Cubes in 3-D Arrays, p. 113
SESSION 1.2 p. 31 **Strategies for Finding Volume** Students discuss strategies for finding the number of cubes (volume) in rectangular prisms. They continue using drawings and written descriptions of boxes to determine the volume of rectangular prisms.	3, 7–10	105, 106–107	• **Dialogue Box:** Understanding Multiplication and Arrays, p. 133
SESSION 1.3 p. 36 **Doubling the Number of Cubes** Given the dimensions of a rectangular prism, students find prisms that hold twice as many cubes as the original box.	11–14	108	• **Dialogue Box:** Common Student Strategies for Doubling, p. 135
SESSION 1.4 p. 41 **How Many Packages?** Students determine how many packages of different sizes will fit in a given box.	15–18	105, 106–107	• **Teacher Note:** Strategies for Finding How Many Packages, p. 115

Ten-Minute Math See page 16 for an overview.

Quick Images: 3-D

- **T25–T28, *Quick Images: 3-D*** (Images 1–14)
- **Connecting cubes** (20 per student)

Estimation and Number Sense

- **M13–M15, Digit Cards**

Materials to Gather	Materials to Prepare
• **T30, Packaging Factory** • **Scissors** (as needed) • **Tape** (as needed) • **Connecting cubes** (20 per student for *Quick Images*, 70 per student for activity)	• **T25–T28, *Quick Images: 3-D*** Cut apart the cube buildings and put Images 1–2 aside for this session. Store cut-apart Transparencies for future use. • **M11, Three-Quarter-Inch Grid Paper** Make copies. (at least 5 per student) • **Demonstration box** From a copy of M11, Three-Quarter-Inch Grid Paper, cut out a pattern for a box with the dimensions $3 \times 4 \times 2$. You will fold and tape the box during the demonstration. • **Cube array** Use connecting cubes to build a cube array with the dimensions $3 \times 4 \times 2$. • **M7–M8, Family Letter** Make copies. (1 per student)
• **M11, Three-Quarter-Inch Grid Paper** (as needed) • **T32, Large Box** • **Connecting cubes** (as needed)	• **M9–M10, Family Letter** Make copies. (1 per student)
• **M11, Three-Quarter-Inch Grid Paper** (as needed) • **Cube array** (from Session 1.1) • **Connecting cubes** (as needed)	
• **T30, Packaging Factory** • **Connecting cubes** (70 per pair) • **Scissors** (as needed) • **Tape** (as needed)	• **M13–M15, Digit Cards** If you do not have Digit Cards from Unit 1, make 1 copy and cut apart cards. Store cut-apart cards for future use. • **M16–M17, How Many Packages? Pattern for Box 1** Make 1 copy, cut out the box pattern, and tape together for session demonstration. Make 1 copy per student and 10 extra copies to use as needed. • **Connecting cube packages** Build one package each of Packages A, B, C, D, and E shown on *Student Activity Book* page 15.

Overhead Transparency

Finding the Volume of Boxes, *continued*

	Student Activity Book	Student Math Handbook	Professional Development: Read Ahead of Time	
SESSION 1.5 p. 48 **Assessment: Finding the Volume of Rectangular Prisms** Students find the volume of rectangular prisms and determine how many packages of different sizes will fit in a given box.	15, 19–22	105, 106–107	• **Teacher Note:** Assessment: Finding the Volume of Rectangular Prisms, p. 117	
SESSION 1.6 p. 54 **Finding Volume** Students continue to find the volume of rectangular prisms, examine doubling and halving the volume of prisms, and determine how many packages of different sizes will fit in a given box.	19–21, 23–26	108		
SESSION 1.7 p. 58 **Designing Boxes** Students design a single box that can be completely filled with each of four or five different-shaped rectangular packages.	27–30	105, 106–107	• **Teacher Note:** Strategies for Designing Boxes, p. 121	

Materials to Gather	Materials to Prepare
• **M11, Three-Quarter-Inch Grid Paper** (as needed) • **Connecting cubes** (70 per pair) • **Box 1** (from Session 1.4)	• **M18, Centimeter Grid Paper** Make copies. (2 copies per student plus extras) • **M19–M20, Assessment: Finding the Volume of Rectangular Prisms** Make copies. (1 per student)
• **M11, Three-Quarter-Inch Grid Paper** (as needed) • **M18, Centimeter Grid Paper** (as needed) • **Box 1** (from Session 1.4) • **Connecting cubes** (70 per pair)	• **M21, How Many Packages? Pattern for Box 2** Make 1 copy, cut out the strips, and tape to Box 1 from Session 1.4. Make 1 copy per student and 10 extra copies to use as needed.
• **M11, Three-Quarter-Inch Grid Paper** (as needed) • **M18, Centimeter Grid Paper** (as needed) • **Connecting cubes** (70 per pair)	

How Many Cubes?

Math Focus Points

- Decomposing 3-D shapes and then recombining them to make a given building
- Determining the number of cubes that will fit into the box made by a given pattern
- Developing a strategy for determining the volume of rectangular prisms

Vocabulary

volume

Today's Plan		Materials
ACTIVITY **1 Introducing *Quick Images: 3-D***	10 MIN CLASS	• T25 * • Connecting cubes
ACTIVITY **2 Introducing How Many Cubes?**	10 MIN CLASS	• T30 • Demonstration box* • Cube array*
ACTIVITY **3 How Many Cubes?**	40 MIN INDIVIDUALS PAIRS	• *Student Activity Book*, pp. 1–3 • Scissors (as needed); tape (as needed); connecting cubes • M11*
SESSION FOLLOW-UP **4 Daily Practice and Homework**		• *Student Activity Book*, pp. 4–5 • *Student Math Handbook*, p. 105 • M7–M8, Family Letter*

*See *Materials to Prepare*, p. 21.

Ten-Minute Math

Quick Images: 3-D **is introduced in this session. Choose a Ten-Minute Math activity from a previous unit, such as *Number Puzzles*, with which your students are familiar.**

1 ACTIVITY
Introducing *Quick Images: 3-D*

10 MIN CLASS

To introduce your students to the new unit, explain to them that they will be learning about geometry for the next three weeks. They will be working with 3-D shapes such as prisms and cylinders and finding the volume of rectangular prisms and other solids.

Tell them that they will begin with a Ten-Minute Math activity called *Quick Images: 3-D.* Each student needs a supply of 20 connecting cubes. All students should be seated facing the overhead projector screen.

Do you remember how we did *Quick Images* in the last unit? We looked at images of dots and found equations to describe the images. This time, we're going to use three-dimensional shapes called cube buildings. Here is how *Quick Images: 3-D* works: I will flash a picture of a cube building on the overhead for 3 seconds. Look at it carefully. When I turn off the overhead, try to see the cube building in your mind. Then use your cubes to make the building that you saw. I will flash the picture again after everyone has had time to try building it.

Display Image 1 from *Quick Images: 3-D* (T25) for three seconds. [It is important to keep the picture up for as close to three seconds as possible.] Give students time to work with their cubes. Once most of the building activity has stopped, call students' attention to the overhead and show the picture again for another three seconds. It is essential to provide enough time between the first and second showings for most students to have completed their building. Students should have done all they can until they see the picture on the screen again.

Be cautious not to show the image for too long or students will build their structure from the picture rather than their mental image of it. At the same time, if you show it too briefly, students do not have time to form a mental image.

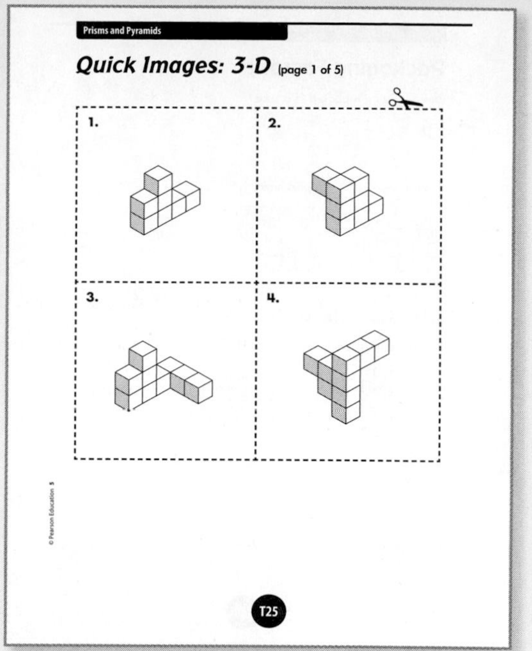

▲ Transparencies, T25

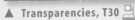

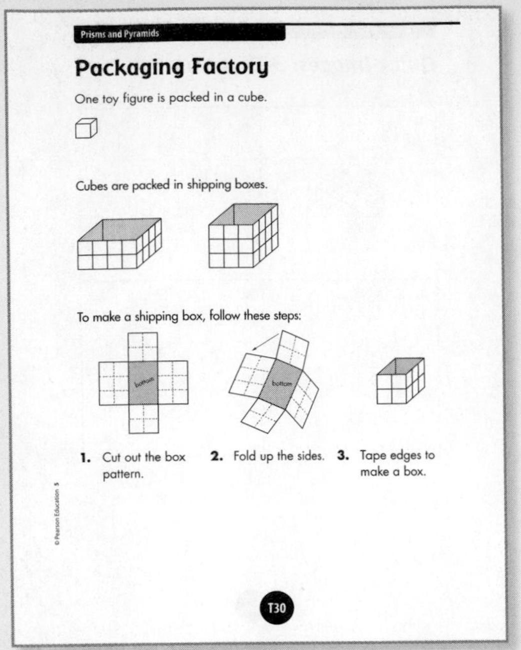
Prisms and Pyramids

Packaging Factory

One toy figure is packed in a cube.

Cubes are packed in shipping boxes.

To make a shipping box, follow these steps:

1. Cut out the box pattern.
2. Fold up the sides.
3. Tape edges to make a box.

T30

▲ Transparencies, T30

Students use cubes to make 3-D buildings.

When the building activity subsides again, show the picture a third time. This time, leave it visible so that all students can complete or revise their solutions.

When students are satisfied that their structures are complete, ask them to describe how they saw the picture as they looked at it in successive flashes. Help students discuss how they were able to remember the whole shape, the parts of the structure, and the relationship among the parts by asking questions such as these:

- How did you see the image?
- Did you break it into different parts? If so, how?
- How were you able to remember what the structure was?

Continue the same activity with Image 2 from *Quick Images: 3-D* (T25). Students continue to work on this Ten-Minute Math activity in the rest of Investigation 1 and in Investigation 3 of this unit.

ACTIVITY

2 Introducing How Many Cubes?

10 MIN CLASS

Display the transparency of Packaging Factory (T30) on the overhead projector, covering the bottom half.

Let's suppose that you are working at a packaging factory. Your company makes cardboard boxes of different shapes and sizes for packing and shipping products.

One product you package is little toy figures. Each toy figure is the same size and is packaged in a little cube.❶ [Point out the cube on the transparency, and hold up one of the connecting cubes.] You often need to ship more than one toy figure at a time, so you pack the cubes in larger shipping boxes. [Point to these on the transparency.] Over the next few days, we're going to work on determining how many cubes will fit in a shipping box and decide whether there's a way that we can figure this out without actually counting each cube.❷

To clarify the task, uncover the bottom half of the transparency. This also introduces the box-pattern diagrams that students will be seeing. Then show the demonstration box pattern you made from grid paper. Show students how the pattern folds into a box, as shown on the transparency. Hold up a single connecting cube and explain that in this investigation, students will use each cube to represent a package of one toy figure.

Place the $3 \times 4 \times 2$ prism you made from connecting cubes inside the box to show how it fits. Note that the cubes must be connected to fit inside the box properly, and the box should be taped so that the sides meet but do not overlap. Point out to students that keeping one side of the pattern untaped makes it easier to place the cubes into the box. Suggest that they do the same when making their patterns.

As you show students how to make the box from grid paper, do not make any suggestions on how students might solve the problems. In this activity, avoid discussing the number of cubes in your box or strategies for finding the number of cubes.

The teacher shows how to build a prism so that connecting cubes fit inside it.

Math Note

❶ **Rectangular Prisms, Boxes, and 3-D Cube Arrays** A geometric solid is a shape that has three dimensions: length, width, and height. In mathematics, these shapes are called *solids,* whether they are filled or hollow. A rectangular prism is a solid with 6 rectangular faces and edges that are perpendicular to one another. In this unit, students work with various representations of rectangular prisms, such as open boxes and congruent layers of cubes arranged in arrays. Each of these representations forms a solid in the shape of a rectangular prism.

Teaching Note

❷ **Clarifying Terminology** To avoid confusion, establish the difference between cubes, packages, and boxes. Single cubes are called *cubes.* Cubes put together into rectangular solids, such as the $3 \times 4 \times 2$ array, are called *packages.* The rectangular boxes made from paper and filled with cubes or packages are called *boxes.*

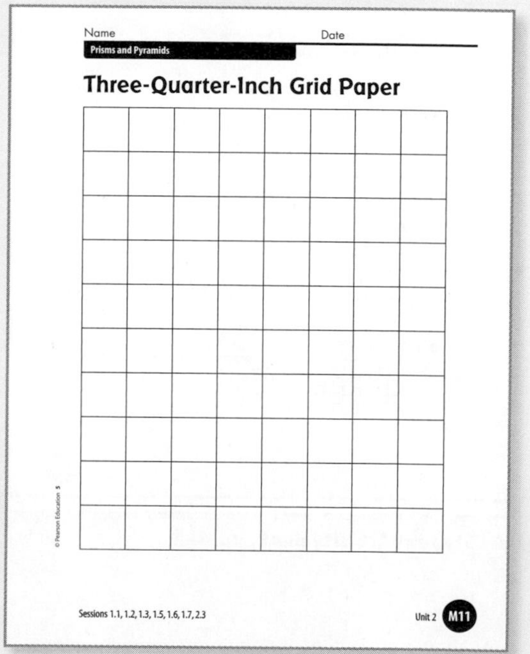

Name Date

Prisms and Pyramids

Three-Quarter-Inch Grid Paper

© Pearson Education 5

Sessions 1.1, 1.2, 1.3, 1.5, 1.6, 1.7, 2.3

Unit 2 M11

▲ **Resource Masters, M11; T31**

Teaching Notes

❸ **Finding Volume** As students build the rectangular prisms to fill the boxes, they are finding the volume of these boxes. However, since the connecting cubes are three-quarter-inch cubes, students record their answers as simply the number of cubes used. This nonstandard unit of measure is used throughout this investigation; standard units of volume are introduced in Investigation 2.

❹ **Checking First Answers** Trying to determine volume before they use the cubes to find answers helps students form and organize mental images or models of the cube arrays. As students check their first answer and actual answer, they refine these models and their ideas about determining the number of cubes that will fit. Encourage students to think about discrepancies between their first answers and the actual count.

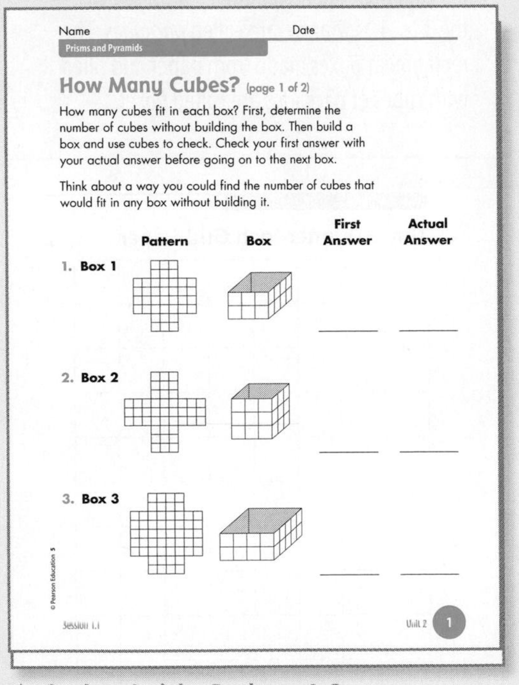
Name Date

Prisms and Pyramids

How Many Cubes? (page 1 of 2)

How many cubes fit in each box? First, determine the number of cubes without building the box. Then build a box and use cubes to check. Check your first answer with your actual answer before going on to the next box.

Think about a way you could find the number of cubes that would fit in any box without building it.

	Pattern	Box	First Answer	Actual Answer
1. Box 1			____	____
2. Box 2			____	____
3. Box 3			____	____

© Pearson Education 5

Session 1.1 Unit 2 1

▲ **Student Activity Book, pp. 1–2**

DIFFERENTIATION: Supporting the Range of Learners

ELL English Language Learners may need help understanding the situational context of this activity. You can gauge how much they already know about factories by asking simple questions.

- What is a factory?
- What objects in this room might have been made in a factory?

Then show students a variety of boxes, bags, and containers to help them understand the concept of *packaging*. Here are some different kinds of packages. What are packages for?

ACTIVITY

40 MIN INDIVIDUALS PAIRS

3 How Many Cubes?

Hand out copies of Three-Quarter-Inch Grid Paper (M11) to the students.

On *Student Activity Book* pages 1–2 you'll find six problems that you're going to solve to find the number of cubes that fit in a box. We'll use these cubes as the unit of measure to find the volume of the box. Here is a picture of a shipping box and a pattern that you can fold up to make the box.❸

Tell students that they will do the following:

- Determine how many cubes fit in the pictured box without building the box and write the first answer in the blank.
- Draw the box pattern on grid paper, cut it out, fold it, and tape the edges to make the box, remembering to leave one side untaped.
- Fill the box with cubes to check their first answer, and then write the actual number of cubes that fit in the box.
- Think about how close their first answer (before building) was to the actual count before going on to the next box.

For each problem, you'll try to figure out the number of cubes each box will hold without building it. Then, use grid paper to make the box, and check the count with cubes. For some boxes, you'll need more than one piece of grid paper to complete the pattern. Before you go on to the next problem, look at your first answer and the actual count.❹ Think about why your first answer was or wasn't close. That way, you'll get better at finding the number of cubes without having to build each box.❺ ❻

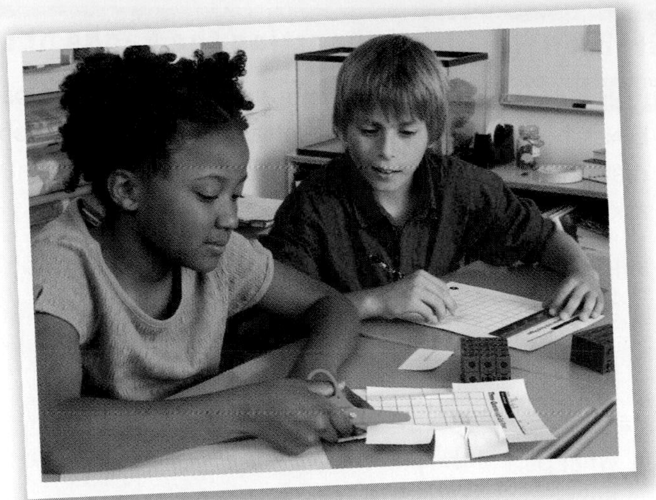

To check their first answer, students build a box to find the actual volume.

When there are about ten minutes left in the session, draw students' attention to *Student Activity Book* page 3.

By now, everyone's had a chance to work on most of the box patterns. Think about how you found the number of cubes that fit in the box before you built each one. On *Student Activity Book* page 3, write your strategy for finding the total number of cubes and for finding the volume of these rectangular prisms without cutting and building. Be as specific as possible. Your method should work for any box, whether you start with a box pattern or the picture of the box. We'll start the next math session by talking about what different strategies you're using.

ONGOING ASSESSMENT: Observing Students at Work

Students find the volume of given boxes.

- **Do students have strategies for determining the number of cubes that will fit in a box without building it?** Are they using the structure of the cube arrays that fill the prism? Are they trying to count each cube individually? Are they trying to use dimensions? Are they using layers?

- **Are students able to use the pattern to construct the box?** If not, what is confusing them? Is it drawing the bottom layer? Is it drawing the sides and understanding how they fold up to form the sides of the prism?

Teaching Note

❺ **Determining Volume With and Without Building Each Box** At the start of Grade 5, some students may have good strategies for accurately determining the volume of each box without actually building each one and filling it with cubes. However, this is important review work for students to ensure that they can visualize and account for all of the space inside each box. Encourage students to explain how each layer or each dimension is accounted for when they use strategies in which they do not cut out and fill each box.

Professional Development

❻ **Teacher Note:** Strategies for Finding the Number of Cubes in 3-D Arrays, p. 113

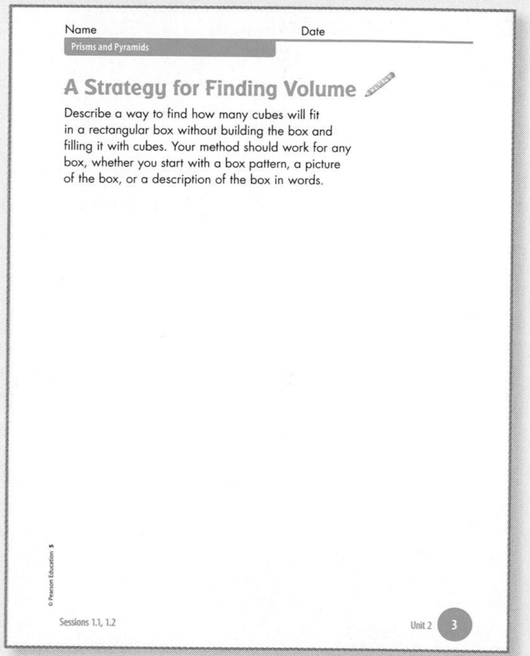
Name Date

Prisms and Pyramids

A Strategy for Finding Volume

Describe a way to find how many cubes will fit in a rectangular box without building the box and filling it with cubes. Your method should work for any box, whether you start with a box pattern, a picture of the box, or a description of the box in words.

© Pearson Education 5

Sessions 1.1, 1.2 Unit 2 3

▲ **Student Activity Book, p. 3** WRITING

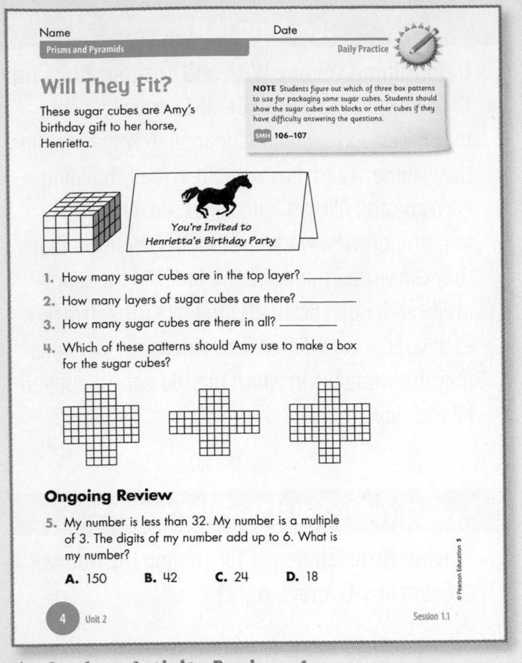
Name Date
Prisms and Pyramids Daily Practice

Will They Fit?

These sugar cubes are Amy's birthday gift to her horse, Henrietta.

NOTE Students figure out which of three box patterns to use for packaging some sugar cubes. Students should show the sugar cubes with blocks or other cubes if they have difficulty answering the questions.

SMH 106–107

You're Invited to Henrietta's Birthday Party

1. How many sugar cubes are in the top layer? ________
2. How many layers of sugar cubes are there? ________
3. How many sugar cubes are there in all? ________
4. Which of these patterns should Amy use to make a box for the sugar cubes?

Ongoing Review

5. My number is less than 32. My number is a multiple of 3. The digits of my number add up to 6. What is my number?

A. 150 **B.** 42 **C.** 24 **D.** 18

© Pearson Education 5

4 Unit 2 Session 1.1

▲ Student Activity Book, p. 4

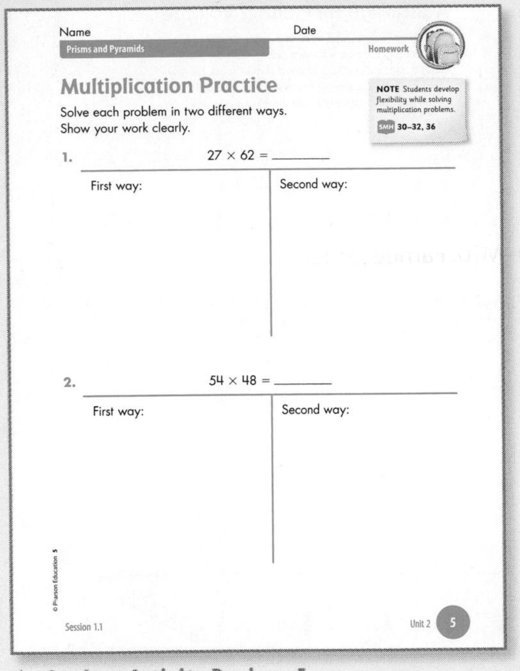
Name Date
Prisms and Pyramids Homework

Multiplication Practice

Solve each problem in two different ways. Show your work clearly.

NOTE Students develop flexibility while solving multiplication problems.

SMH 30–32, 36

1. 27 × 62 = ________

First way: Second way:

2. 54 × 48 = ________

First way: Second way:

© Pearson Education 5

Session 1.1 Unit 2 5

▲ Student Activity Book, p. 5

DIFFERENTIATION: Supporting the Range of Learners

Intervention Students may not understand how the patterns fold into boxes, how parts of a pattern correspond to parts of a box, or how to draw the pictured pattern on grid paper. For students having difficulties, ask questions such as these:

- Is the pattern you've drawn on the grid paper exactly like the one pictured?
- Does each part of your pattern (bottom, sides) match the same parts in the pictured pattern?
- What part of the pattern will make [point to a side on the picture of the box] this side of the box?

Extension Encourage students who are successfully drawing a pattern to explain their strategy to other students.

4 SESSION FOLLOW-UP
Daily Practice and Homework

Daily Practice: For reinforcement of this unit's content, have students complete *Student Activity Book* page 4.

Homework: Students solve multiplication problems in two ways on *Student Activity Book* page 5.

Student Math Handbook: Students and families may use *Student Math Handbook* page 105 for reference and review. See pages 141–143 in the back of this unit.

Family Letter: Send home copies of Family Letter (M7–M8).

SESSION 1.2

Strategies for Finding Volume

Math Focus Points

- Designing patterns for boxes that hold a given number of cubes
- Finding the volume of rectangular prisms
- Developing a strategy for determining the volume of rectangular prisms

Vocabulary

rectangular prism
dimension

Today's Plan		Materials
DISCUSSION **1 Strategies for Finding Volume**	10 MIN CLASS	• *Student Activity Book,* p. 3 (from Session 1.1)
ACTIVITY **2 Finding Volume**	35 MIN INDIVIDUALS	• *Student Activity Book,* pp. 7–8 • M11 • Connecting cubes
DISCUSSION **3 Finding Volume**	15 MIN CLASS PAIRS	• T32
SESSION FOLLOW-UP **4 Daily Practice and Homework**		• *Student Activity Book,* pp. 9–10 • *Student Math Handbook,* pp. 105, 106–107 • M9–M10, Family Letter*

*See *Materials to Prepare,* p. 21.

Ten-Minute Math

Quick Images: 3-D Show Images 3–5 from *Quick Images: 3-D* (T25–T26) and follow the procedure for the basic routine. For each image, students discuss how they built their structures, including any revisions they made after each viewing. Ask students:

- How did you remember the parts of the image?
- What did you notice about the relationship of the parts of the image?
- What helped you remember the whole image so that you could build your structure?

Teaching Note

❶ **Using the Word *Dimensions*** If students naturally begin to use the word *dimensions* as they talk about the boxes, incorporate it into classroom use. This term is formally introduced to students in Session 1.3.

Professional Development

❷ **Dialogue Box:** Understanding Multiplication and Arrays, p. 133

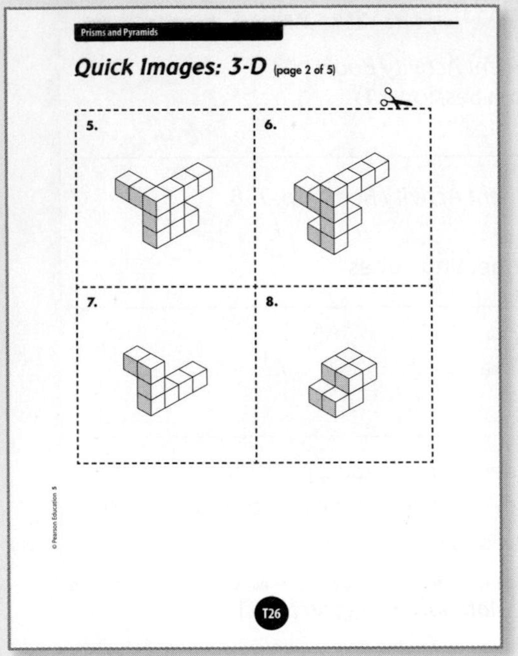

▲ Transparencies, T26

DISCUSSION

1 Strategies for Finding Volume

10 MIN CLASS

Math Focus Points for Discussion

- Developing a strategy for determining the volume of rectangular prisms

At the end of the lesson yesterday, everyone wrote a strategy for finding the volume of any rectangular prism. As you listen to your classmates explaining their strategies, your job is to think about what they're saying and to see whether your strategy is similar or different. Remember that the strategy you present should work for any box, so try not to use specific numbers in your explanations.❶

Call on several different students to explain their strategies. For each explanation, ask questions such as

- Does anyone have questions?
- Will this strategy work for any box? How do you know?
- Who has a similar strategy?
- Who has a different strategy?

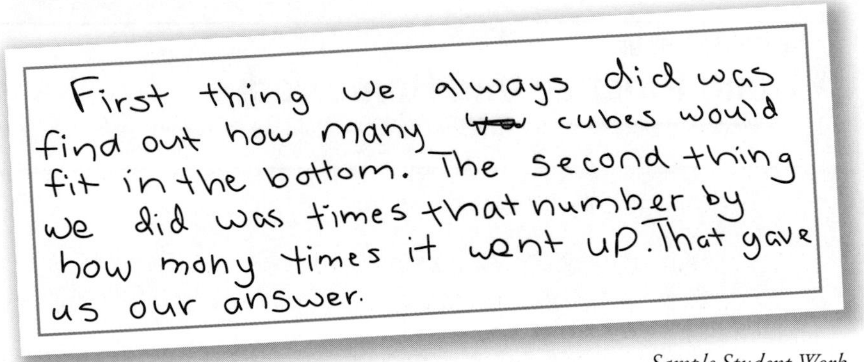
First thing we always did was find out how many ~~to~~ cubes would fit in the bottom. The second thing we did was times that number by how many times it went up. That gave us our answer.

Sample Student Work

Today, you're going to find the volume of more boxes. You may have just heard a strategy that you want to use to determine the number of cubes that fill the box, or you may want to refine the strategy you're already using.❷

2 ACTIVITY

Finding Volume

35 MIN INDIVIDUALS

Students complete *Student Activity Book* pages 7–8. These pages include problems in which only the box is pictured or only words are used to describe the box. Students design the patterns for Problems 3–5. Remind students they may need more than one sheet of grid paper to complete the pattern.

Students use their understanding of volume to draw patterns of boxes.

ONGOING ASSESSMENT: Observing Students at Work

Students find the volume for given boxes.

- **Are students able to determine the number of cubes without building the actual rectangular prism that fits inside the box?**
- **Are students using a strategy to determine the total number of cubes?** What is the strategy? Is it efficient (e.g., using multiplication or skip counting)?
- **Do students understand the structure of the rectangular prism (e.g., the prism is composed of layers—either horizontal or vertical)?**
- **Are students able to draw the box pattern?** If not, what is confusing them? Is it drawing the bottom layer? Is it drawing the sides and understanding how they fold up to form the sides of the prism?

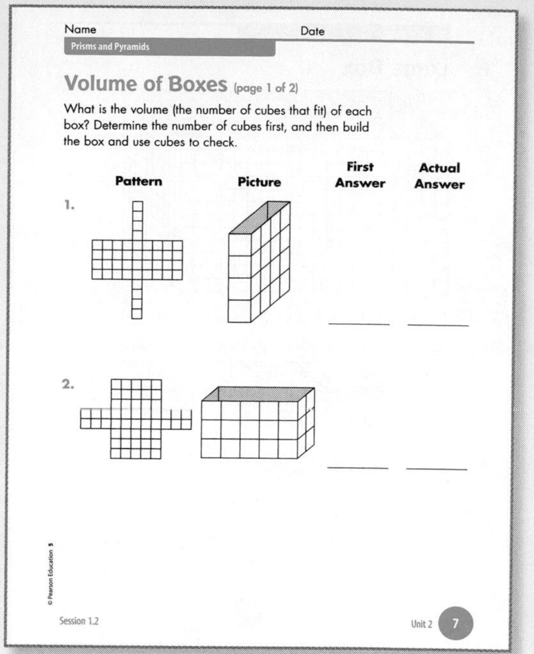

Name Date

Prisms and Pyramids

Volume of Boxes (page 1 of 2)

What is the volume (the number of cubes that fit) of each box? Determine the number of cubes first, and then build the box and use cubes to check.

	Pattern	Picture	First Answer	Actual Answer
1.			____	____
2.			____	____

© Pearson Education 5

Session 1.2 Unit 2 7

▲ Student Activity Book, p. 7

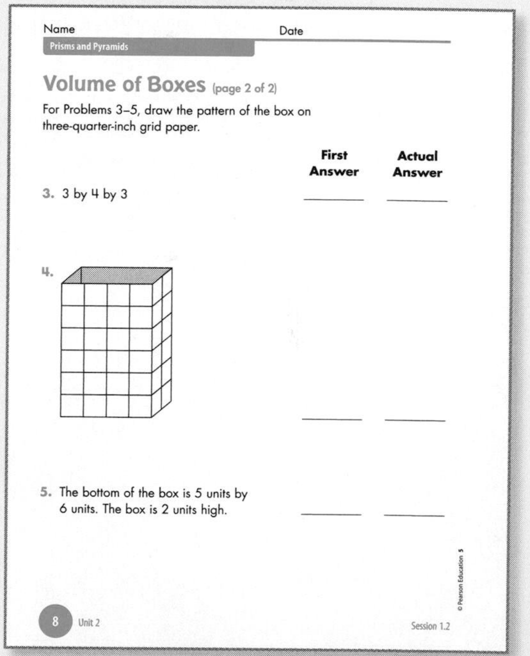

Name Date

Prisms and Pyramids

Volume of Boxes (page 2 of 2)

For Problems 3–5, draw the pattern of the box on three-quarter-inch grid paper.

	First Answer	Actual Answer
3. 3 by 4 by 3	____	____
4.	____	____
5. The bottom of the box is 5 units by 6 units. The box is 2 units high.	____	____

© Pearson Education 5

8 Unit 2 Session 1.2

▲ Student Activity Book, p. 8

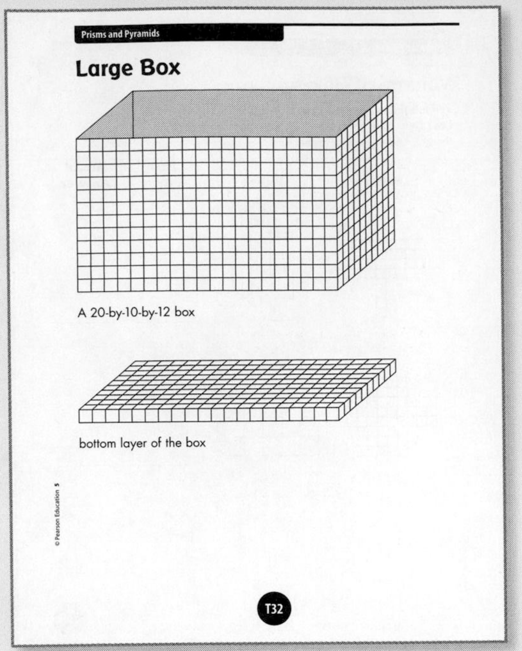

▲ Transparencies, T32

DIFFERENTIATION: Supporting the Range of Learners

Intervention Some students will have a difficult time seeing how the structure of the rectangular prisms is related to a strategy that works for any box. Help them see the connection between the pattern, the prism that the pattern makes, and a strategy for finding the volume of any rectangular prism. Ask questions such as these:

- How many layers does the box have?
- How many cubes are in a layer?
- How many rows of squares do you need on each side of the pattern to show how many layers the cube box has?
- How can you use this information to think about a strategy for finding the number of cubes of any box?

If some students are having difficulty drawing the box pattern for Problem 3, help them focus on the structure of the box by asking questions such as the following:

- How many cubes form the bottom layer of this box? How can you show the bottom layer on the grid paper?
- How many layers does this box contain? How can you draw the sides to show the number of layers?

3 DISCUSSION

15 MIN CLASS PAIRS

Finding Volume

Math Focus Points for Discussion

◆ Developing a strategy for determining the volume of rectangular prisms

Students have been working for two days to find the volume of rectangular prisms. They have also been considering a strategy that they can use to determine the volume of any rectangular prism. In this discussion, students are asked to find the volume of a prism when given only a description. They do not build the box or the 3-D array of cubes. They use their understanding of the dimensions of either the box or the 3-D cube arrays (layers) that form the congruent layers of the prism.

Find the number of cubes that fit in a box that is 20 units by 10 units on the bottom and 12 units high. How can you convince the rest of the class that your answer is correct?

Students share their strategies for finding the volume of a large box.

Give students about five minutes to solve this problem and, if time allows, to compare results with a neighbor. After students have been working for a few minutes, display the transparency of Large Box (T32) on the overhead to give students a visual clue of what the box looks like.

Ask students to explain their solutions. Ask questions such as these:

- How many cubes are in the bottom layer? How do you know?
- How many layers are there? How do you know?
- How many cubes will fit in the box? How do you know?

4 SESSION FOLLOW-UP
Daily Practice and Homework

Daily Practice: For ongoing review, have students complete *Student Activity Book* page 9.

Homework: Students determine the number of cubes (volume) for different boxes on *Student Activity Book* page 10.

Student Math Handbook: Students and families may use *Student Math Handbook* pages 105, 106–107 for reference and review. See pages 141–143 in the back of this unit.

Family Letter: Send home copies of Family Letter (M9–M10).

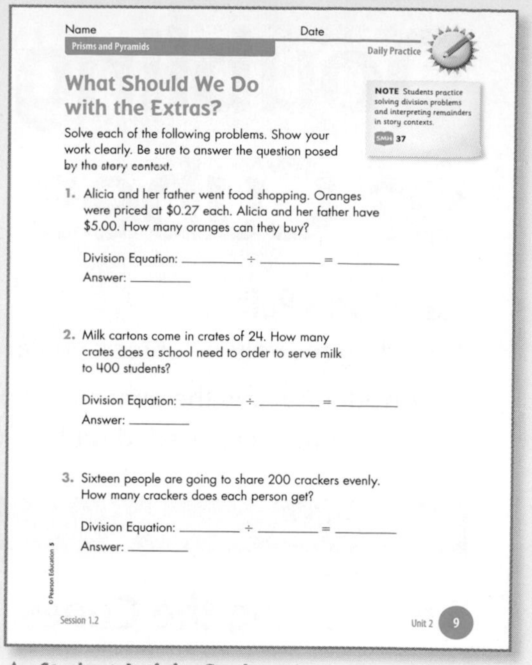

Name Date

Prisms and Pyramids — Daily Practice

What Should We Do with the Extras?

NOTE Students practice solving division problems and interpreting remainders in story contexts.

SMH 37

Solve each of the following problems. Show your work clearly. Be sure to answer the question posed by the story context.

1. Alicia and her father went food shopping. Oranges were priced at $0.27 each. Alicia and her father have $5.00. How many oranges can they buy?

   Division Equation: ______ ÷ ______ = ______

   Answer: ______

2. Milk cartons come in crates of 24. How many crates does a school need to order to serve milk to 400 students?

   Division Equation: ______ ÷ ______ = ______

   Answer: ______

3. Sixteen people are going to share 200 crackers evenly. How many crackers does each person get?

   Division Equation: ______ ÷ ______ = ______

   Answer: ______

© Pearson Education 5

Session 1.2 Unit 2 9

▲ **Student Activity Book, p. 9**

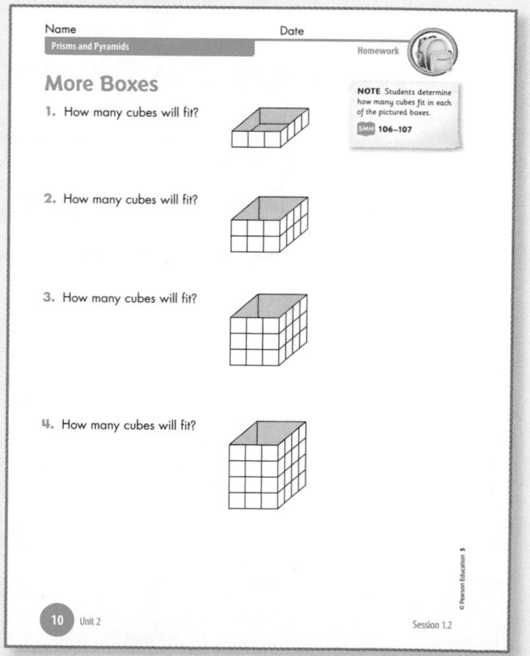

Name Date

Prisms and Pyramids — Homework

More Boxes

NOTE Students determine how many cubes fit in each of the pictured boxes.

SMH 106–107

1. How many cubes will fit?
2. How many cubes will fit?
3. How many cubes will fit?
4. How many cubes will fit?

© Pearson Education 5

10 Unit 2 Session 1.2

▲ **Student Activity Book, p. 10**

Doubling the Number of Cubes

Math Focus Points

- Finding the volume of rectangular prisms
- Considering how the dimensions of a box change when the volume is changed (doubled, halved, or tripled)

Today's Plan		Materials
ACTIVITY **1 Doubling the Cubes**	45 MIN PAIRS INDIVIDUALS	• *Student Activity Book*, p. 11 • M11 • Cube array (from Session 1.1) • Connecting cubes
DISCUSSION **2 What Are the Dimensions?**	15 MIN CLASS	• *Student Activity Book*, p. 11
SESSION FOLLOW-UP **3 Daily Practice and Homework**		• *Student Activity Book*, pp. 12–14 • *Student Math Handbook*, p. 108

Ten-Minute Math

Quick Images: 3-D Show Images 6–8 from *Quick Images: 3-D* (T26) and follow the procedure for the basic routine. For each image, students discuss how they built their structures, including any revisions they made after each viewing. Ask students:

- How did you remember the parts of the image?
- What did you notice about the relationship of the parts of the image?
- What helped you remember the whole image so that you could build your structure?

1 ACTIVITY
Doubling the Cubes

45 MIN PAIRS INDIVIDUALS

Briefly explain to students how dimensions can be used to describe the rectangular prisms they have built from cubes. Remind students how they labeled the dimensions of the arrays they used earlier in the year. Tell them that similar notation can be used to describe the dimensions of 3-D objects.

Hold up the 3 × 4 × 2 cube array.

If we wanted to describe the dimensions of this prism, what three numbers would we use? (3, 4, 2) What do the numbers represent? (the unit of measure, e.g., 3 units)

Remind students that dimensions can be written with an "x", which in this case means "by" and not "times" (e.g., 3 × 4 × 2), and write the dimensions as 3 × 4 × 2 on the board. As you say the numbers, point to each dimension on the rectangular prism.

For the purposes of the activities you'll be working on, the order of the numbers isn't really important. What is important is that you know what each of the numbers represents. Some of you may say that the prism is 3 × 4 × 2, others may say 2 × 3 × 4, and others may even describe the prism by saying that it is 3 × 4 on the bottom and 2 high.

Direct students' attention to *Student Activity Book* page 11.❶

The Packaging Factory wants us to build a box that holds twice as many cubes as a 2 × 3 × 5 box. See how many boxes you can find that will hold twice as many cubes. Be sure to list the dimensions on your *Student Activity Book* page. You may work on your own or with a partner.❷

Observe students to see whether they double the number of cubes and then figure out the dimensions or whether they double one or more of the dimensions to see how many cubes are needed.

Students may refer to "Changing the Dimensions" in their *Student Math Handbook.*

Teaching Note

❶ **Have Materials Available** As they work on this problem, students should use whatever materials they feel comfortable working with (e.g., cubes, grid paper, blank paper). Some students may want to design the pattern and build each box, and others may simply draw a rough pattern on blank paper.

Professional Development

❷ **Dialogue Box:** Common Student Strategies for Doubling, p. 135

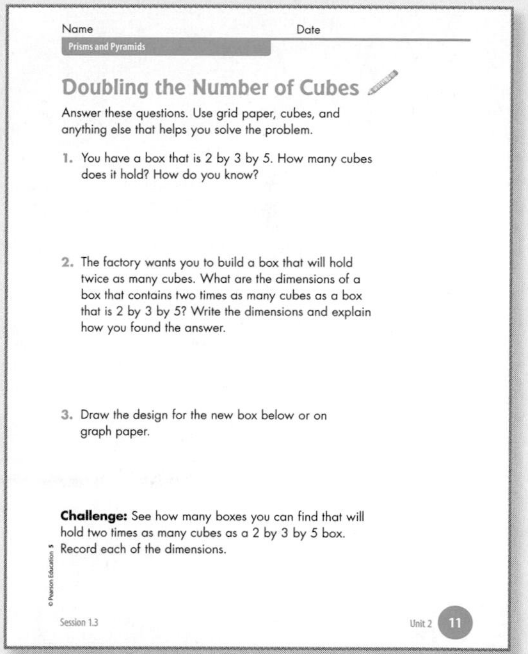
Name Date

Prisms and Pyramids

Doubling the Number of Cubes

Answer these questions. Use grid paper, cubes, and anything else that helps you solve the problem.

1. You have a box that is 2 by 3 by 5. How many cubes does it hold? How do you know?

2. The factory wants you to build a box that will hold twice as many cubes. What are the dimensions of a box that contains two times as many cubes as a box that is 2 by 3 by 5? Write the dimensions and explain how you found the answer.

3. Draw the design for the new box below or on graph paper.

Challenge: See how many boxes you can find that will hold two times as many cubes as a 2 by 3 by 5 box. Record each of the dimensions.

© Pearson Education 5

Session 1.3 Unit 2 11

▲ **Student Activity Book, p. 11** WRITING

Math Note

③ **Doubling the Number of Cubes** The goal for this activity is for students to see the connection between changing the dimensions of a box and changing the number of cubes that fit in the box. One way to double the number of cubes is to double *one* of the original dimensions, but there are other ways. Some students may explain that they simply looked for sets of 3 numbers that multiply together to get 60; others may explain they started with a layer of 10 and then determined how many layers they needed to have 60 cubes.

Students build boxes that can hold twice the number of cubes.

ONGOING ASSESSMENT: Observing Students at Work

Students explore the relationship between the dimensions of a box and doubling the number of cubes in the box.③

- **Do students understand the relationship between a change in one dimension of a box and the volume of the box (e.g., doubling one dimension doubles the volume)?**
- **How do students solve this problem?**

DISCUSSION

2 What Are the Dimensions?

15 MIN CLASS

Math Focus Points for Discussion

- Considering how the dimensions of a box change when the volume is changed (doubled, halved, or tripled)

What are the dimensions of the boxes you found that will hold twice as many cubes as the 2 × 3 × 5 box?

As students suggest dimensions, list them for the class to see. Ask whether everyone agrees that those dimensions would work. Ask how many students got the same answer.

Original Dimensions 2 × 3 × 5	
4 × 3 × 5	1 × 5 × 12
2 × 6 × 5	5 × 2 × 6
10 × 6 × 1	2 × 3 × 10
1 × 1 × 60	2 × 2 × 15
3 × 10 × 2	3 × 4 × 5

What do you notice about these dimensions? Talk to a neighbor about what you notice.

After a few minutes, ask students to explain what they noticed. Students are likely to notice such things as these:

- The product of each set of dimensions equals 60.
- Each dimension is a factor of 60.
- Some of the same numbers (2, 4, 5) show up in all the dimensions.

In some of the dimensions listed, only one dimension is doubled. If no student mentions it, circle the dimensions on the chart that are variations of $4 \times 3 \times 5$, $2 \times 6 \times 5$, and $2 \times 3 \times 10$ (e.g., these dimensions written in any order), and ask students what they notice.

[Tamira] says that she noticed that in these dimensions I just circled, two of the dimensions are the same as the original box. Any thoughts about that? [Olivia] says that she agrees and that the dimension that changed is doubled. What do you think about that? [Felix] has a conjecture. He thinks that if you want to double the volume of a box, you need to double only one dimension. You may want to think about that as we do more of this work.

If no student brings it up, ask whether anyone started by doubling each of the dimensions.

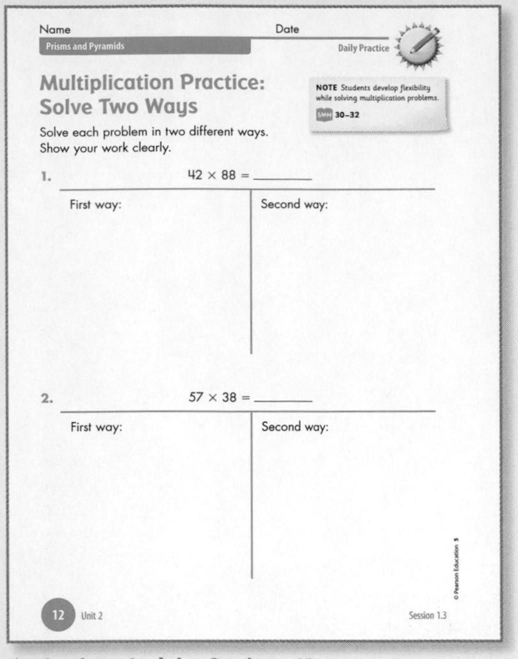

Name Date

Prisms and Pyramids — Daily Practice

Multiplication Practice: Solve Two Ways

NOTE Students develop flexibility while solving multiplication problems.

SMH 30–32

Solve each problem in two different ways. Show your work clearly.

1. 42 × 88 = ______

First way: Second way:

2. 57 × 38 = ______

First way: Second way:

© Pearson Education 5

12 Unit 2 Session 1.3

▲ Student Activity Book, p. 12

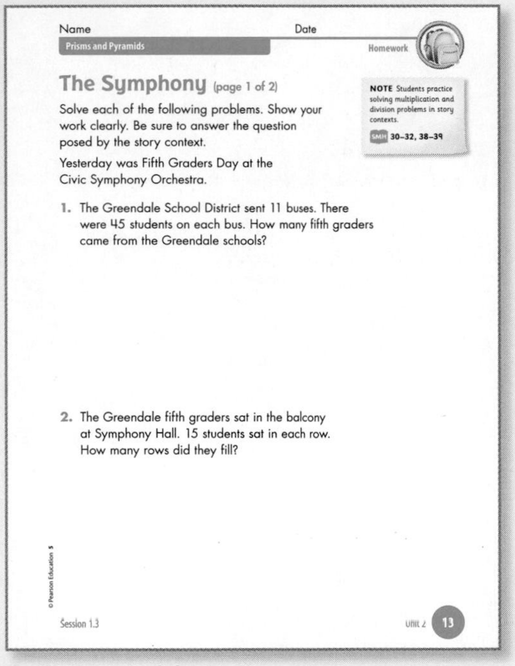

Name Date

Prisms and Pyramids — Homework

The Symphony (page 1 of 2)

NOTE Students practice solving multiplication and division problems in story contexts.

SMH 30–32, 38–39

Solve each of the following problems. Show your work clearly. Be sure to answer the question posed by the story context.

Yesterday was Fifth Graders Day at the Civic Symphony Orchestra.

1. The Greendale School District sent 11 buses. There were 45 students on each bus. How many fifth graders came from the Greendale schools?

2. The Greendale fifth graders sat in the balcony at Symphony Hall. 15 students sat in each row. How many rows did they fill?

© Pearson Education 5

Session 1.3 Unit 2 13

▲ Student Activity Book, p. 13

[Olivia] says that she and [Walter] doubled all three of the dimensions. They started by thinking that the new dimensions would be 4 × 6 × 10, but they then realized that was 240 cubes! How much did they increase the total number of cubes? [Hana] says that it's 8 times because 8 × 30 = 240. There's something else interesting to think about—why did doubling all three of the dimensions increase the total number of cubes eight times?

Some students are ready to consider that doubling each dimension increases the volume by 8 times or that doubling two of the dimensions increases the volume by 4 times. Students ready to do so can investigate this idea further during Sessions 1.5 (pages 48–53) and 1.6 (pages 54–57).

SESSION FOLLOW-UP

3 Daily Practice and Homework

Daily Practice: For ongoing review, have students complete *Student Activity Book* page 12.

Homework: On *Student Activity Book* pages 13–14, students use multiplication and division to solve story problems.

Student Math Handbook: Students and families may use *Student Math Handbook* page 108 for reference and review. See pages 141–143 in the back of this unit.

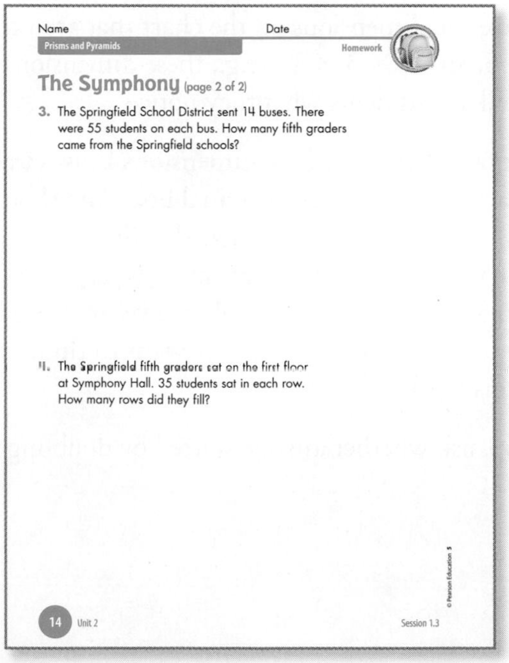

Name Date

Prisms and Pyramids — Homework

The Symphony (page 2 of 2)

3. The Springfield School District sent 14 buses. There were 55 students on each bus. How many fifth graders came from the Springfield schools?

4. The Springfield fifth graders sat on the first floor at Symphony Hall. 35 students sat in each row. How many rows did they fill?

© Pearson Education 5

14 Unit 2 Session 1.3

▲ Student Activity Book, p. 14

How Many Packages?

Math Focus Points

- Organizing rectangular packages to fit in rectangular boxes

Today's Plan		Materials
ACTIVITY 1 Introducing *Estimation and Number Sense*	10 MIN CLASS	• M13–M15
ACTIVITY 2 Differently-Sized Packages	40 MIN CLASS INDIVIDUALS	• *Student Activity Book*, p. 15 • T30 (from Session 1.1); M16–M17* • Connecting cube packages*; connecting cubes; scissors; tape • Box 1 (for demonstration)*
DISCUSSION 3 How Many Packages?	10 MIN CLASS	• *Student Activity Book*, p. 15
SESSION FOLLOW-UP 4 Daily Practice and Homework		• *Student Activity Book*, pp. 16–18 • *Student Math Handbook*, pp. 105, 106–107

*See *Materials to Prepare*, p. 21.

Ten-Minute Math

NOTE: The Ten-Minute Math activity for this unit, *Estimation and Number Sense*, is introduced in this session. Plan to do today's Ten-Minute Math sometime after math class, or if it is not possible, choose a Ten-Minute Math activity from a previous unit, such as *Number Puzzles*, with which your students are familiar.

Estimation and Number Sense Using Digit Cards, create two, 2-digit by 2-digit *multiplication* problems, (__ __ × __ __). Give students 30 seconds to mentally estimate a product as close as possible to the exact answer. Students may jot down partial products if they wish. Some students may be able to determine the exact answer. Have two or three students explain their work, and record these strategies on the board or overhead.

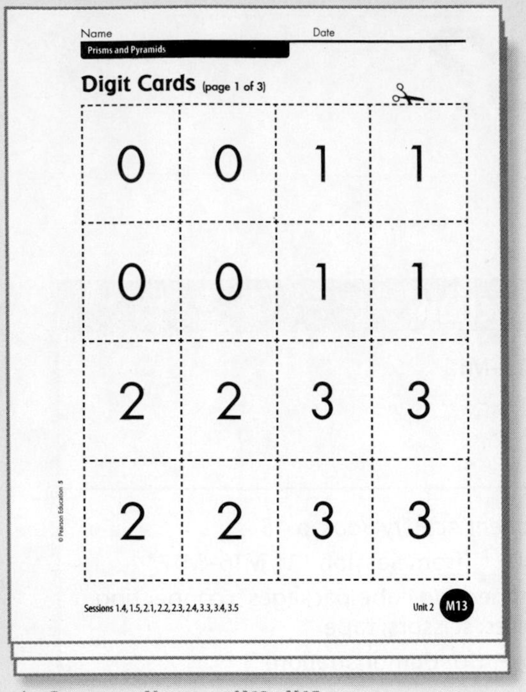
Name Date
Prisms and Pyramids
Digit Cards (page 1 of 3)

0	0	1	1
0	0	1	1
2	2	3	3
2	2	3	3

© Pearson Education 5
Sessions 1.4, 1.5, 2.1, 2.2, 2.3, 2.4, 3.3, 3.4, 3.5 Unit 2 M13

▲ Resource Masters, M13–M15

ACTIVITY

1 Introducing *Estimation and Number Sense*

10 MIN CLASS

Introduce a new Ten-Minute Math activity, *Estimation and Number Sense.*

We'll do this Ten-Minute Math activity often this year to practice mental computation and estimation. I'll give you a problem to solve, and you'll have 30 seconds to solve as much of it as you can.

Show students a template showing a 2-digit by 2-digit multiplication problem.

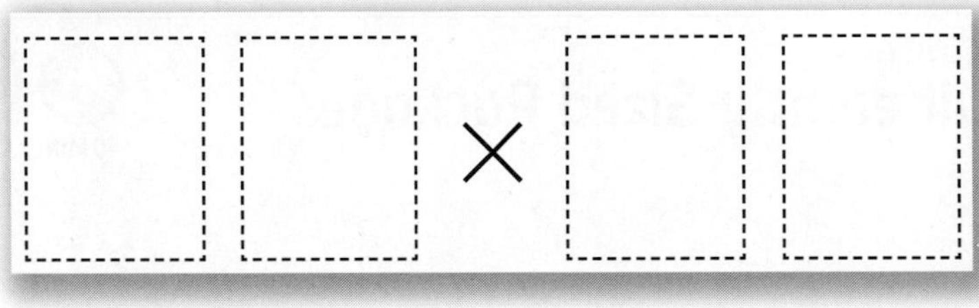

I'll draw cards from a deck of Digit Cards to make the multiplication problem. When you first see the problem, make a quick estimate of what you think the product is to help give you an idea of a reasonable answer. Then, try to solve as much of the problem as you can until I tell you that time is up. Here's the first problem:

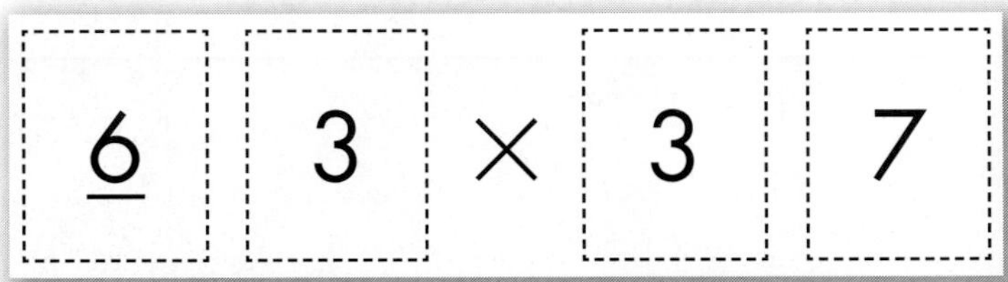

Give students approximately 30 seconds to first estimate and then mentally solve as much of this problem as possible. Students may jot down partial solutions but should not use pencil and paper to solve the problem. After 30 seconds, ask for students' answers and write them on the board.

Here are some answers that students got: (1,800, 2,400, 2,310). Who can explain how they got their answer?

Students might say:

"I did 60 × 30 and got 1,800."

"I did 60 × 40 and got 2,400."

"First I did 63 × 30; that was 1,890. Then I did 7 × 60 and that was 420. It took me a while to add: it was hard to do it in my head. I got 2,310 and we were out of time. But all I have to do is add 21 more (7 × 3) to get the answer."

These numbers weren't very friendly, so it was hard to do much of it mentally. But do your best to do more than just an initial estimate, such as 60 × 30 or 60 × 40. The exact answer to this problem is 2,331.

Use the Digit Cards to create another problem.

4	1	×	1	9

These numbers look a little easier. Do your best to find the exact answer.

After 30 seconds or so, collect students' answers and write them on the board. Ask students to explain their answers.

Students might say:

"I did 41 × 20 and got 820. Then I tried to do more, but I ran out of time."

"I did 41 × 20 and got 820. I knew that it was one group of 41 more, so I took 41 away from 820. First I took 40 away and that's 780, then I took one more away and that's 779."

"I took the wrong thing away. I got 820, too, then I took 19 away and that was 801."

If additional time remains, present another problem.

Math Note

❶ **Understanding the Dimensions of Rectangular Prisms** In this new activity, students use a "package" that is not a cubic unit to further their understanding of the structure of rectangular prisms. Many students are able to find the number of cubes to fill the box in the first three sessions but are still developing their conceptual understanding of volume as the amount of space filled by a given solid. By using different-sized packages (2 x 2 x 2, 1 x 3 x 1, 2 x 2 x 1, 2 x 2 x 3, and 5 x 1 x 1), students must consider all three dimensions of rectangular prisms.

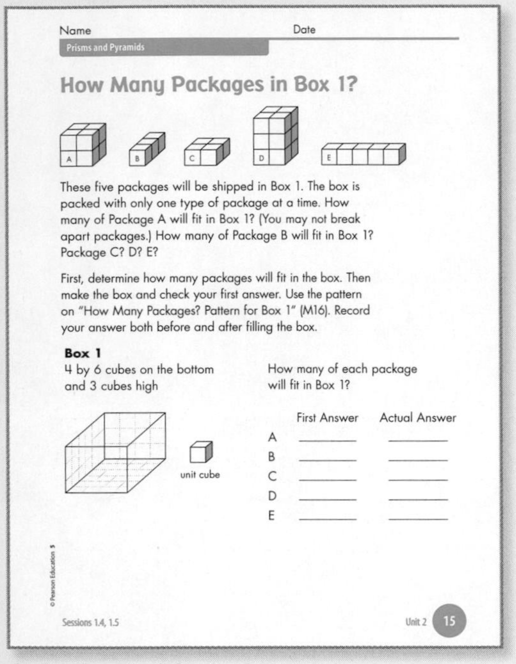
Name Date

Prisms and Pyramids

How Many Packages in Box 1?

These five packages will be shipped in Box 1. The box is packed with only one type of package at a time. How many of Package A will fit in Box 1? (You may not break apart packages.) How many of Package B will fit in Box 1? Package C? D? E?

First, determine how many packages will fit in the box. Then make the box and check your first answer. Use the pattern on "How Many Packages? Pattern for Box 1" (M16). Record your answer both before and after filling the box.

Box 1
4 by 6 cubes on the bottom and 3 cubes high

unit cube

How many of each package will fit in Box 1?

	First Answer	Actual Answer
A	______	______
B	______	______
C	______	______
D	______	______
E	______	______

© Pearson Education 5

Sessions 1.4, 1.5 Unit 2 15

▲ **Student Activity Book, p. 15**

ACTIVITY

2 Differently-Sized Packages

40 MIN CLASS INDIVIDUALS

In this activity, students consider situations in which paper boxes are filled with rectangular packages that are made with several cubes, instead of just one cube. To avoid confusion, it is important to maintain the distinction between cubes, packages, and boxes. If necessary, use Packaging Factory (T30) to review this language with students.❶

Show students the actual cube packages A–E from *Student Activity Book* page 15 and Box 1 from How Many Packages? Pattern for Box 1 (M16–M17) as you introduce this new activity.

Here we are on the job at a packaging factory. We're going to make boxes to ship different quantities of these five packages. Before, our "package" was only one cube, but now the "packages" have more than one cube.

Show students how the five packages correspond to Packages A, B, C, D, and E on *Student Activity Book* page 15. Distribute copies of How Many Packages? Pattern for Box 1 (M16–M17). To construct the box, students first cut out the $6 \times 4 \times 1$ pattern on M16 and tape it. Then, they cut out the two 10×2 strips on M17 to complete the $6 \times 4 \times 3$ box. They fill it with different types of packages.

Your job is to determine how many of each package will fit in a box before it is made. For now, you will put only one kind of package in the box. For example, first you'll find how many of Package A will fit in the box. Then you'll find how many of Package B will fit in the box, and so on. The *Student Activity Book* page is similar to what you've been doing. First, you'll try to determine the number of each package that will fit in the box, before you build. Then you'll build the package(s) to see whether you are correct. Do them one at a time. That way, you'll get better at finding accurate answers without building boxes.

At the end of the session today, we'll discuss Package A. You will have more time in the Math Workshop in the next two sessions to continue working on these problems.

If students cannot find the correct number of packages without building the packages and boxes, encourage them to reflect on their work and develop a better strategy.

- You determined [9] for Package A, but only [6] actually fit. Why do you think your strategy did not work?
- Is each package going to fill the box all the way to the top?
- Will some packages fit better than others? How can you tell?

In checking their answers, some students will completely fill the boxes with packages. Others may make only one package and move it around in the bottom of the box to determine the number in a layer.

Students can check and adjust their answers by building models.

Instruct students to save Box 1 work in the next two sessions.❷

ONGOING ASSESSMENT: Observing Students at Work

Students find the number of rectangular packages that fit in a box.

- **How close are students' first answers to the actual quantities?** As they consider the problem, are they able to visualize how the different packages fit inside the box?
- **Are students considering the relationship of Packages C and D?** Do they notice that Package C is one layer of Package D?
- **How are students finding the actual number of packages?** Do they build one package, and then position it in different locations in the box? Do they build all the packages to fit in the box?

Professional Development

❷ **Teacher Note:** Strategies for Finding How Many Packages?, p. 115

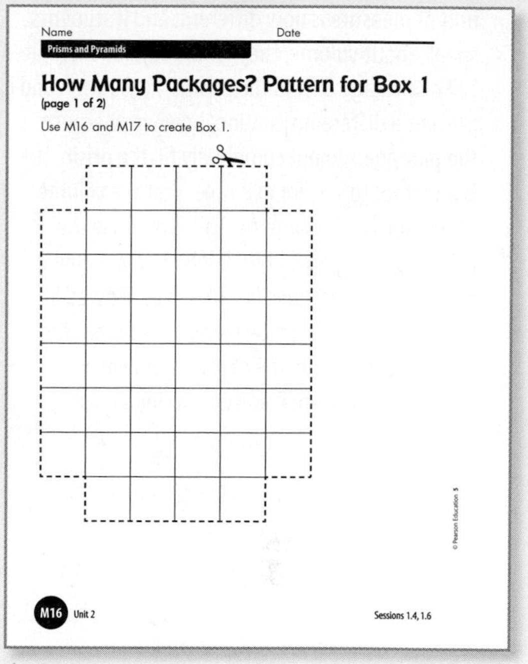

Name Date

Prisms and Pyramids

How Many Packages? Pattern for Box 1
(page 1 of 2)

Use M16 and M17 to create Box 1.

M16 Unit 2 Sessions 1.4, 1.6

© Pearson Education 5

▲ Resource Masters, M16

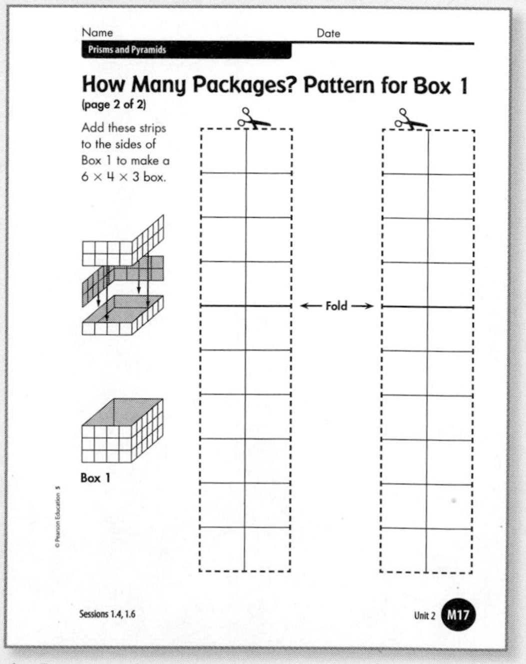

Name Date

Prisms and Pyramids

How Many Packages? Pattern for Box 1
(page 2 of 2)

Add these strips to the sides of Box 1 to make a 6 × 4 × 3 box.

Sessions 1.4, 1.6 Unit 2 M17

© Pearson Education 5

▲ Resource Masters, M17

Math Note

❸ **Volume of Packages** In using these different-sized packages, students are still finding the volume of the rectangular prisms. However, the unit of measure is now different, and if students speak about volume, they would say, for example, "24 of Package B fit in the prism." Packages A and E present a different situation, however, because the packages do not completely fill the prism. It is incorrect to say, for example, that the volume of the box is 6 Package As. This is because the box is not completely filled. If it were possible to break up the packages (which is not allowed in the activity), it would be correct to say that the volume is the same as 9 of the volume of Package A. Package E presents a similar situation.

Circulate as students are working, and ask questions such as these:

- How many of Package [A] do you think will fit? Why?
- Can you turn Package [A] a different way? Will that make a difference? How?
- Do the packages completely fill the box? How much space is left?
- Can you use the dimensions of the big box to help you? How?
- What relationships do you notice between the packages? Does knowing how many of Package C fit in the box help you figure out how many of Package D fit? How?

DIFFERENTIATION: Supporting the Range of Learners

Intervention If some students are struggling with Package A and are confused because there will be an "empty layer" in the box, encourage them to start with Package D. Have them put one package in the box and ask them how many they think will fit. If they seem unsure, have them build another Package D, place it in the box, and ask again how many more they think will fit. Encourage them to explain their thinking.

DISCUSSION

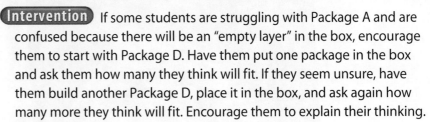

3 How Many Packages?

10 MIN CLASS

Math Focus Points for Discussion

- Organizing rectangular packages to fit in rectangular boxes

When there are ten minutes remaining in the session, bring the class together for a discussion. Remind students that it is all right if they have not finished *Student Activity Book* page 15 yet. They will have more time during the next two sessions to complete this work.

Ask students to explain their strategy for finding how many of Package A fit into the box. Students may have built with cubes to model the situation, drawn on grid paper, visualized placing packages in the box, and so on. As students explain their strategies, they should describe and show what they did, using the packages and Box 1.❸

Who will explain a strategy for finding how many of Package A fit in the box? Your explanation should include describing your thinking and showing the materials you worked with. You need to convince everyone that your strategy is a valid strategy.

Student strategies may include the following:

- Building the packages one at a time and putting them in the box until no more fit
- Building one package and then moving it around in the box to see how packages will fit
- Visualizing both the package and the box and determining the total number of packages

4 SESSION FOLLOW-UP
Daily Practice and Homework

Daily Practice: For ongoing review, have students complete *Student Activity Book* page 16–17.

Homework: Students find different ways to multiply two or more numbers to find given products on *Student Activity Book* page 18.

Student Math Handbook: Students and families may use *Student Math Handbook* pages 105, 106–107 for reference and review. See pages 141–143 in the back of this unit.

Name Date

Prisms and Pyramids Daily Practice

Closest Estimate (page 1 of 2)

NOTE Students practice strategies for estimating products.

SMH 30–32

Each problem below has a choice of three estimates. Which one do you think is closest? Choose the closest estimate *without* solving the problem. Circle the closest estimate. Then write about why you think this estimate is the closest.

1. The closest estimate for 84×19 is ______.

   1,600 1,800 2,000

   I think this is the closest because:

2. The closest estimate for 49×28 is ______.

   1,400 1,500 1,600

   I think this is the closest because:

16 Unit 2 Session 1.4

© Pearson Education 5

▲ Student Activity Book, p. 16

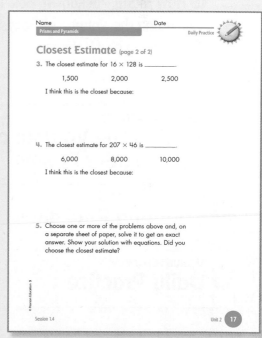

Name Date

Prisms and Pyramids Daily Practice

Closest Estimate (page 2 of 2)

3. The closest estimate for 16×128 is ______.

   1,500 2,000 2,500

   I think this is the closest because:

4. The closest estimate for 207×46 is ______.

   6,000 8,000 10,000

   I think this is the closest because:

5. Choose one or more of the problems above and, on a separate sheet of paper, solve it to get an exact answer. Show your solution with equations. Did you choose the closest estimate?

© Pearson Education 5

Session 1.4 Unit 2 17

▲ Student Activity Book, p. 17

Name Date

Prisms and Pyramids Homework

Factors of 160 and 240

NOTE Students practice finding multiplication expressions with two numbers and with more than two numbers for 160 and 240.

SMH 33–34

Using whole numbers, find all the ways to multiply to make each product. First, find the ways with two numbers, and then find ways to multiply with more than two numbers.

1. Multiplying to make 160

Ways to multiply with two numbers: Example: 16×10	Ways to multiply with more than two numbers: Example: $2 \times 8 \times 10$

2. Multiplying to make 240

Ways to multiply with two numbers:	Ways to multiply with more than two numbers:

© Pearson Education 5

18 Unit 2 Session 1.4

▲ Student Activity Book, p. 18

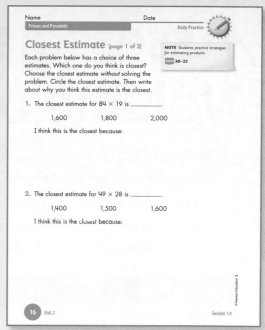

Assessment: Finding the Volume of Rectangular Prisms

Math Focus Points

- Finding the volume of rectangular prisms
- Organizing rectangular packages to fit in rectangular boxes
- Considering how the dimensions of a box change when the volume is changed (doubled, halved, or tripled)

Today's Plan		Materials
MATH WORKSHOP **1 Finding Volume** 1A How Many Packages? Box 1 1B Finding the Volume of Boxes 1C Doubling and Halving	35 MIN	1A • *Student Activity Book*, p. 15 • Connecting cubes; Box 1 (from Session 1.4) 1B • *Student Activity Book*, p. 19 • M18 1C • *Student Activity Book*, pp. 20–21 • M11 • Connecting cubes
ASSESSMENT ACTIVITY **2 Finding the Volume of Rectangular Prisms**	10 MIN INDIVIDUALS	• M19–M20*
DISCUSSION **3 Counting Packages**	15 MIN CLASS	• *Student Activity Book*, pp. 15, 20 • Box 1 (from Session 1.4)
SESSION FOLLOW-UP **4 Daily Practice**		• *Student Activity Book*, p. 22 • *Student Math Handbook*, pp. 105, 106–107

*See *Materials to Prepare*, p. 21.

Ten-Minute Math

Estimation and Number Sense Using Digit Cards, create two 2-digit by 2-digit *multiplication* problems, (___ × ___). Give students 30 seconds to mentally estimate a product as close as possible to the exact answer. Students may jot down partial products if they wish. Some students may be able to determine the exact answer. Have two or three students explain their work and record these strategies on the board or overhead.

1 MATH WORKSHOP

Finding Volume

35 MIN

Students spend the next two math sessions in Math Workshop, where they continue finding the volume of rectangular prisms and considering the relationship between the number of cubes that fill the prism and the dimensions of the prism. There is an assessment at the end of this session.

1A How Many Packages? Box 1

INDIVIDUALS

Students continue working on *Student Activity Book* page 15 from Session 1.4.

Tell students that the discussion at the end of the session will focus on using Packages C and D to fill Box 1.

For a full description of this activity, see Session 1.4, page 44.

DIFFERENTIATION: Supporting the Range of Learners

Intervention Some students are still working on their understanding of volume (that cubes filling a rectangular prism can be decomposed into congruent layers and that volume can be determined by finding the number of cubes in one layer and multiplying that by the number of layers). These students benefit from doing *Student Activity Book* page 15, which helps them think about all three dimensions of the prism, but they should spend more time on Activity 1B.

1B Finding the Volume of Boxes

INDIVIDUALS

Direct students' attention to *Student Activity Book* page 19, on which they are given dimensions of prisms and asked to find the volume and draw patterns for two of the prisms. These problems involve bigger numbers and students are not expected to build the 3-D cube arrays. Give students the option of drawing the patterns on Centimeter Grid Paper (M18), or drawing them on blank paper. Students who are still developing their understanding of the structure of 3-D cube arrays to find the volume of rectangular prisms should spend more time on this activity.

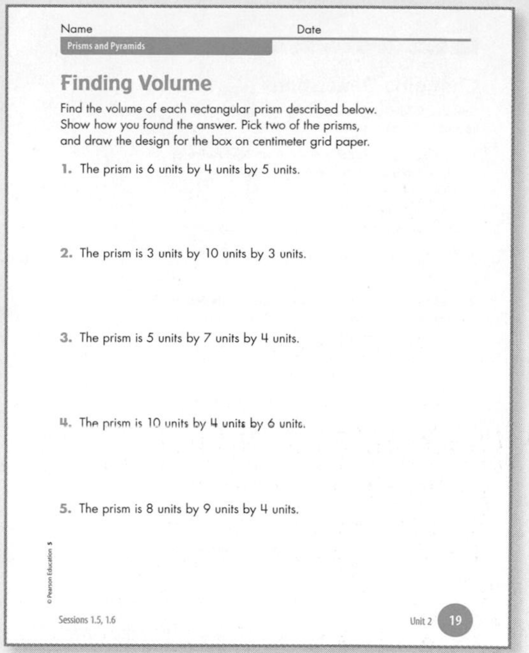

Name Date

Prisms and Pyramids

Finding Volume

Find the volume of each rectangular prism described below. Show how you found the answer. Pick two of the prisms, and draw the design for the box on centimeter grid paper.

1. The prism is 6 units by 4 units by 5 units.
2. The prism is 3 units by 10 units by 3 units.
3. The prism is 5 units by 7 units by 4 units.
4. The prism is 10 units by 4 units by 6 units.
5. The prism is 8 units by 9 units by 4 units.

© Pearson Education 5

Sessions 1.5, 1.6 Unit 2 19

▲ Student Activity Book, p. 19 PORTFOLIO

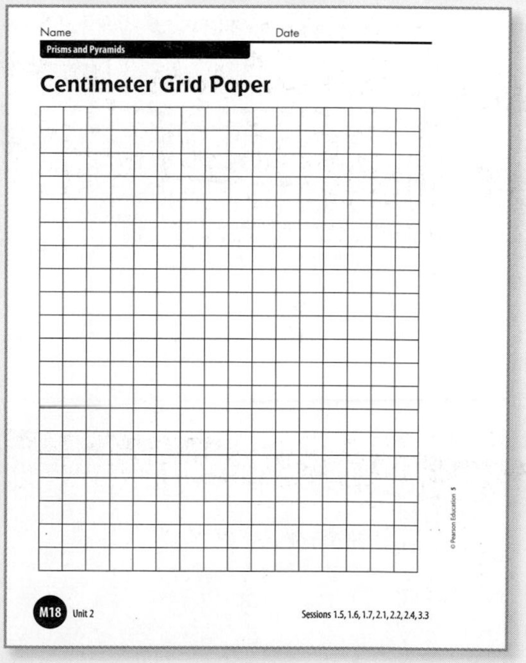

Name Date

Prisms and Pyramids

Centimeter Grid Paper

© Pearson Education 5

M18 Unit 2 Sessions 1.5, 1.6, 1.7, 2.1, 2.2, 2.4, 3.3

▲ Resource Masters, M18

Name Date

Prisms and Pyramids

Changing Dimensions (page 1 of 2)

Solve the following problems using any material that will help you find the answer.

1. Find the dimensions of a box that will hold **twice** as many cubes as a box that is 2 by 6 by 4.
   Volume of original box: ________
   Volume of new box: ________
   Dimensions of new box: ________
   Explain how you found the dimensions of the new box.

2. Find the dimensions of a box that will hold **twice** as many cubes as a box that is 4 by 2 by 9.
   Volume of original box: ________
   Volume of new box: ________
   Dimensions of new box: ________
   Explain how you found the dimensions of the new box.

3. Find the dimensions of a box that will hold **twice** as many cubes as a box that is 4 by 5 by 6.
   Volume of original box: ________
   Volume of new box: ________
   Dimensions of new box: ________
   Explain how you found the dimensions of the new box.

20 Unit 2 Sessions 1.5, 1.6

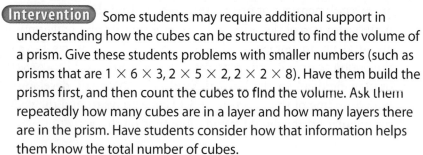

▲ **Student Activity Book, p. 20** WRITING

Students use different strategies to find the volume of boxes with larger dimensions.

ONGOING ASSESSMENT: Observing Students at Work

Students find volume and draw box patterns for rectangular prisms.

- **How are students finding the volume of these prisms?** Are they using the dimensions and multiplying length by width by height? Are they finding the number of cubes in a layer and multiplying the number of layers?
- **Are students able to draw the box pattern?** If not, what is confusing them? Is it drawing the bottom layer? Is it drawing the sides and understanding how they fold up to form the sides of the prism?

DIFFERENTIATION: Supporting the Range of Learners

Intervention Some students may require additional support in understanding how the cubes can be structured to find the volume of a prism. Give these students problems with smaller numbers (such as prisms that are $1 \times 6 \times 3$, $2 \times 5 \times 2$, $2 \times 2 \times 8$). Have them build the prisms first, and then count the cubes to find the volume. Ask them repeatedly how many cubes are in a layer and how many layers there are in the prism. Have students consider how that information helps them know the total number of cubes.

Extension Students who require a challenge should investigate and explain why doubling all of the dimensions creates eight times the volume (or halving all the dimensions creates $\frac{1}{8}$ the volume).

Extension Students who understand how to find volume should spend more time on Activities 1A and 1C.

1C Doubling and Halving

INDIVIDUALS

On *Student Activity Book* pages 20–21, students are given dimensions of rectangular prisms and asked to find the dimensions of prisms that hold double and half the number of cubes of the original prism.①

ONGOING ASSESSMENT: Observing Students at Work

Students explore the relationship between the dimensions of a box and doubling or halving the number of cubes in the box.

- **Do students understand the relationship between changing the dimensions of a box and how many cubes will fit in the box?**
- **How do students solve this problem?** Do they double or halve the number of cubes and then figure out what the dimensions could be? Do they double or halve one or more of the dimensions to see how many cubes would be needed?

DIFFERENTIATION: Supporting the Range of Learners

Intervention If students are unable to complete this task without concrete models, give them smaller models to work with. For example, ask them to build a $2 \times 3 \times 4$ three-dimensional cube array and find the volume. Have them build a second $2 \times 3 \times 4$ prism, put it next to the first one, and determine the dimensions. Ask them whether the volume is now doubled. A similar procedure can be used for halving the volume.

Intervention Students who are still consolidating ideas about volume should spend most of their time on Activities 1A and 1B during this session.

Teaching Note

① **Using the Dimensions of the Original Box** Some students solve these problems by finding the volume of the original prism and then looking for three numbers to multiply to equal that number. Acknowledge that they are getting correct answers, but ask them to focus on thinking about how they could change the original dimensions to find new ones.

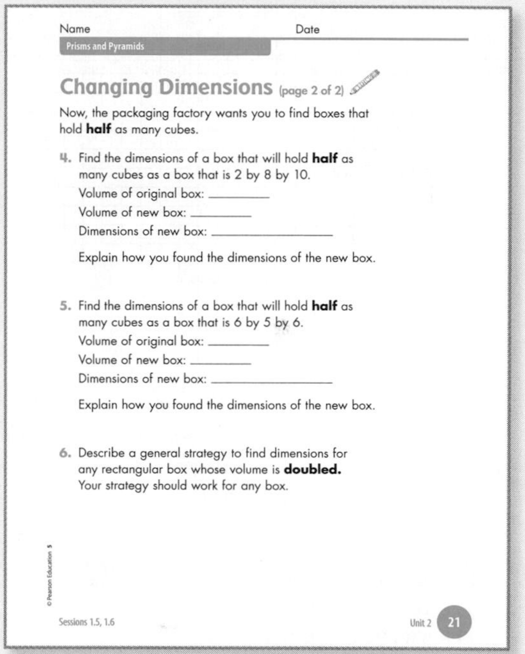

Name Date

Prisms and Pyramids

Changing Dimensions (page 2 of 2)

Now, the packaging factory wants you to find boxes that hold **half** as many cubes.

4. Find the dimensions of a box that will hold **half** as many cubes as a box that is 2 by 8 by 10.
Volume of original box: ________
Volume of new box: ________
Dimensions of new box: ________
Explain how you found the dimensions of the new box.

5. Find the dimensions of a box that will hold **half** as many cubes as a box that is 6 by 5 by 6.
Volume of original box: ________
Volume of new box: ________
Dimensions of new box: ________
Explain how you found the dimensions of the new box.

6. Describe a general strategy to find dimensions for any rectangular box whose volume is **doubled.** Your strategy should work for any box.

© Pearson Education 5

Sessions 1.5, 1.6 Unit 2 21

▲ Student Activity Book, p. 21 WRITING

Professional Development

❷ **Teacher Note:** Assessment: Finding the Volume of Rectangular Prisms, p. 117

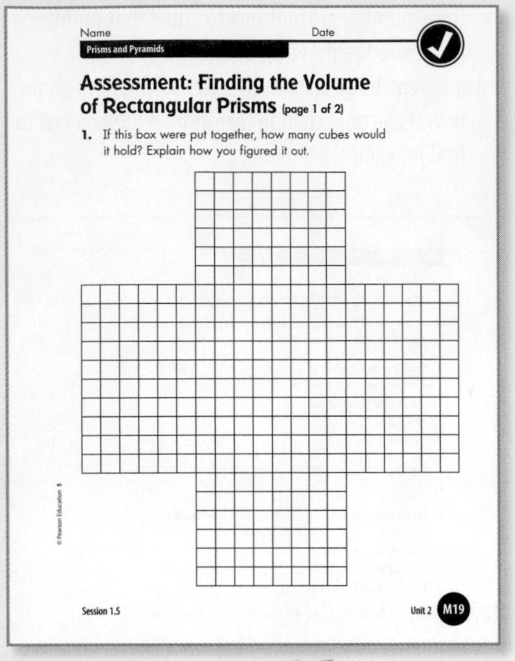
Name Date
Prisms and Pyramids
Assessment: Finding the Volume of Rectangular Prisms (page 1 of 2)

1. If this box were put together, how many cubes would it hold? Explain how you figured it out.

© Pearson Education 5

Session 1.5 Unit 2 M19

▲ Resource Masters, M19 PORTFOLIO

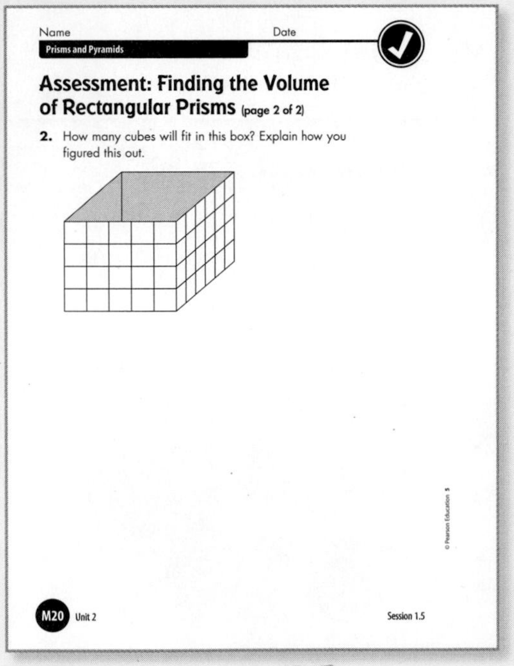
Name Date
Prisms and Pyramids
Assessment: Finding the Volume of Rectangular Prisms (page 2 of 2)

2. How many cubes will fit in this box? Explain how you figured this out.

© Pearson Education 5

M20 Unit 2 Session 1.5

▲ Resource Masters, M20 PORTFOLIO

ASSESSMENT ACTIVITY

2 Finding the Volume of Rectangular Prisms

10 MIN INDIVIDUALS

Students complete Assessment: Finding the Volume of Rectangular Prisms (M19–M20).❷ This assessment addresses Benchmark 1: Find the volume of rectangular prisms. Students find the number of cubes that will fit in a given box pattern. They find the volume of a rectangular prism.

Students who finish early can continue working on the Math Workshop activities.

DISCUSSION

3 Counting Packages

15 MIN CLASS

Math Focus Points for Discussion

- Organizing rectangular packages to fit in rectangular boxes

Instruct students to return their attention to *Student Activity Book* page 15. Ask them to explain their strategy for finding how many of Package C fit into Box 1. Students may have built packages with cubes to model the situation, drawn on grid paper, visualized placing packages in the box, or used other strategies. As students explain their strategies, they should show and describe what they did, using the "packages" and Box 1.

Who will explain a strategy for finding how many of Package C fits in the first box? Your explanation should include describing your thinking and showing the materials you worked with. You need to convince everyone that your answer is correct.

Students might say:

"I built one Package C and pictured how it would fit on the bottom of the box. Six packages would fit on the bottom layer, and there would be three layers. So 18 Package Cs fill the box."

"I got 18, too, but I did it a little differently. I stood the packages up so that the first 12 of them would fit in the box. Then I could lay 6 of them flat on top of those 12. So it's 18 packages."

Repeat the procedure with Package D.

Students might say:

"I pictured how it would fit in the box. Package D is the same height as the box, and 6 of them would fit and completely fill the box."

"I tried to lay Package D on its side, but it wouldn't fit the box."

If no student brings it up, ask students whether knowing how many of Package C filled the box helps them know how many of Package D would fit.

Is there any relationship between Package C and Package D that helps you find how many fit in the box?

Students might say:

"I noticed that Package D is like three of Package C, so the box can hold only $\frac{1}{3}$ the number of Package Ds. That's $18 \div 3 = 6$."

Tell students to save Box 1 for use in Session 1.6.

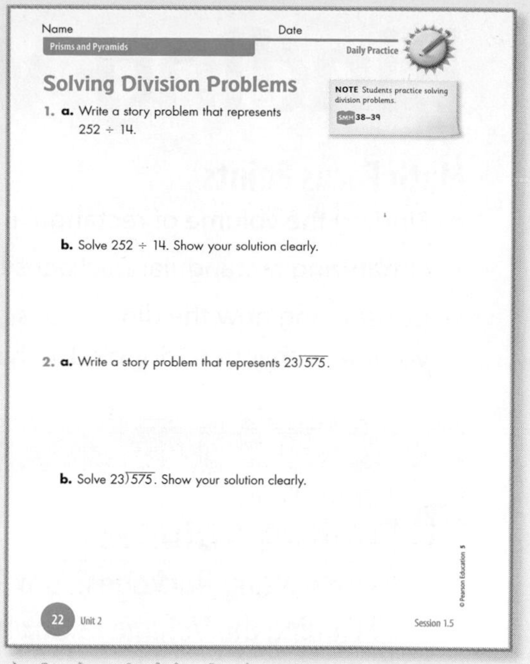

Name Date

Prisms and Pyramids — Daily Practice

Solving Division Problems

NOTE Students practice solving division problems.

SMH 38–39

1. a. Write a story problem that represents $252 \div 14$.

b. Solve $252 \div 14$. Show your solution clearly.

2. a. Write a story problem that represents $23\overline{)575}$.

b. Solve $23\overline{)575}$. Show your solution clearly.

© Pearson Education 5

22 Unit 2 Session 1.5

▲ Student Activity Book, p. 22

4 SESSION FOLLOW-UP
Daily Practice

Daily Practice: For ongoing review, have students complete *Student Activity Book* page 22.

Student Math Handbook: Students and families may use *Student Math Handbook* pages 105, 106–107 for reference and review. See pages 141–143 in the back of this unit.

Finding Volume

Math Focus Points

- Finding the volume of rectangular prisms
- Organizing rectangular packages to fit in rectangular boxes
- Considering how the dimensions of a box change when the volume is changed (doubled, halved, or tripled)

Today's Plan		Materials
1 MATH WORKSHOP **Finding Volume** **1A How Many Packages? Box 2** **1B Finding the Volume of Boxes** **1C Doubling and Halving**	45 MIN	**1A** • *Student Activity Book,* p. 23 • M21*; Box 1 (from Session 1.4) • Connecting cubes **1B** • *Student Activity Book,* p. 19 (from Session 1.5) • M18 **1C** • *Student Activity Book,* pp. 20–21 (from Session 1.5) • M11 • Connecting cubes
2 DISCUSSION **Changing Dimensions**	15 MIN CLASS	• *Student Activity Book,* pp. 20–21 (from Activity 1C; completed)
3 SESSION FOLLOW-UP **Daily Practice and Homework**		• *Student Activity Book,* pp. 24–26 • M11 • *Student Math Handbook,* p. 108

*See *Materials to Prepare,* p. 23.

Ten-Minute Math

Quick Images: 3-D **Show Images 9–11 from *Quick Images: 3-D* (T27) and follow the procedure for the basic routine. For each image, students discuss how they built their structures, including any revisions they made after each viewing. Ask students:**

- How did you remember the parts of the image?
- What did you notice about the relationship of the parts of the image?
- What helped you remember the whole image so that you could build your structure?

1 MATH WORKSHOP
Finding Volume

45 MIN

Students complete activities from the Math Workshop that began in Session 1.5. Inform students that the discussion at the end of today's session focuses on *Student Activity Book* pages 20 and 21, so everyone should work on those pages for part of the time today. Students who performed well on the Assessment given in Session 1.5 should spend most of their time in this session on Activities 1A and 1C. Students who are still working on finding volume should spend most of their time on Activity 1B and some time on Activity 1C.

1A How Many Packages? Box 2

INDIVIDUALS

From M21, students cut out two layers to add to Box 1, thus creating Box 2 (dimensions are now $4 \times 6 \times 5$). Show students the Box 2 you made from adding the strips from M21 to the model of Box 1 from Session 1.4. On *Student Activity Book* page 23, students determine how many of Packages A, D, and E will fit in the new box. Because one dimension is now 5, Packages A and D will not completely fill the box (with no gaps), but Package E, which did not completely fill Box 1, will completely fill Box 2. Their thinking in this activity will help them as they work on Design a Box in Session 1.7.

1B Finding the Volume of Boxes

INDIVIDUALS

For a full description of this activity, see Session 1.5, page 49.

1C Doubling and Halving

INDIVIDUALS

For a full description of this activity, see Session 1.5, page 51.

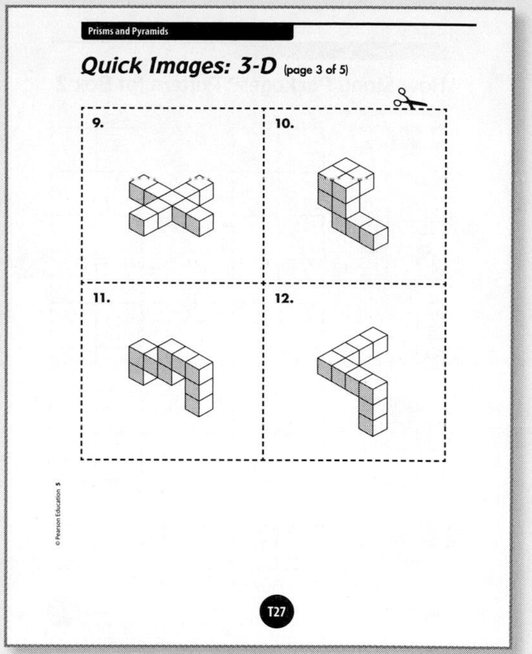
Prisms and Pyramids

Quick Images: 3-D (page 3 of 5)

9. 10. 11. 12.

© Pearson Education 5

T27

▲ Transparencies, T27

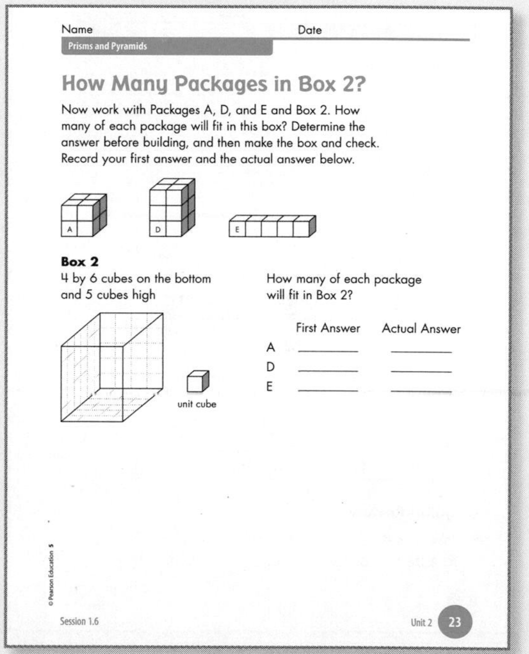
Name Date

Prisms and Pyramids

How Many Packages in Box 2?

Now work with Packages A, D, and E and Box 2. How many of each package will fit in this box? Determine the answer before building, and then make the box and check. Record your first answer and the actual answer below.

Box 2
4 by 6 cubes on the bottom and 5 cubes high

unit cube

How many of each package will fit in Box 2?

	First Answer	Actual Answer
A		
D		
E		

© Pearson Education 5

Session 1.6 Unit 2 23

▲ Student Activity Book, p. 23

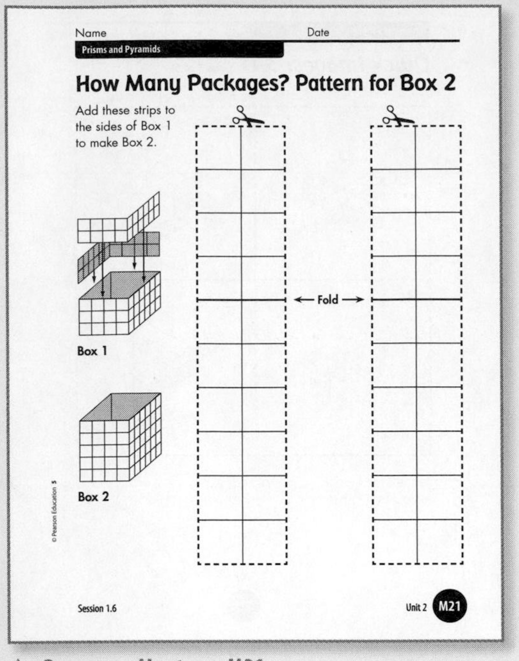
Name Date

Prisms and Pyramids

How Many Packages? Pattern for Box 2

Add these strips to the sides of Box 1 to make Box 2.

Fold

Box 1

Box 2

© Pearson Education 5

Session 1.6 Unit 2 M21

▲ Resource Masters, M21

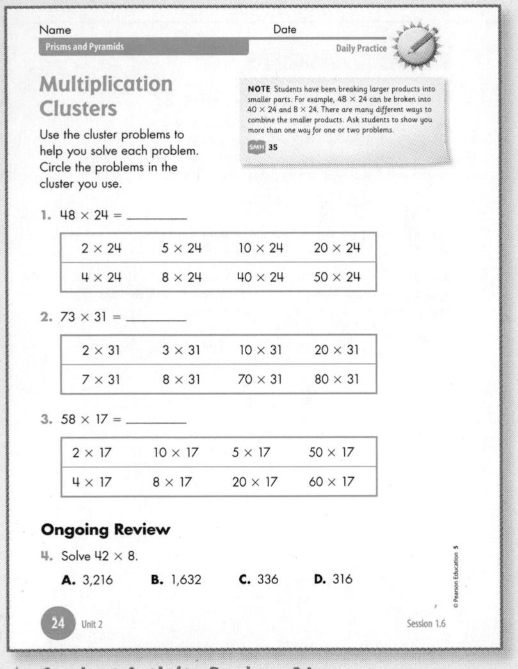
Name Date

Prisms and Pyramids

Daily Practice

Multiplication Clusters

Use the cluster problems to help you solve each problem. Circle the problems in the cluster you use.

NOTE Students have been breaking larger products into smaller parts. For example, 48 × 24 can be broken into 40 × 24 and 8 × 24. There are many different ways to combine the smaller products. Ask students to show you more than one way for one or two problems.

SMH 35

1. 48 × 24 = ______

2 × 24	5 × 24	10 × 24	20 × 24
4 × 24	8 × 24	40 × 24	50 × 24

2. 73 × 31 = ______

2 × 31	3 × 31	10 × 31	20 × 31
7 × 31	8 × 31	70 × 31	80 × 31

3. 58 × 17 = ______

2 × 17	10 × 17	5 × 17	50 × 17
4 × 17	8 × 17	20 × 17	60 × 17

Ongoing Review

4. Solve 42 × 8.

A. 3,216 B. 1,632 C. 336 D. 316

© Pearson Education 5

24 Unit 2 Session 1.6

▲ Student Activity Book, p. 24

DISCUSSION

2 Changing Dimensions

15 MIN CLASS

Math Focus Points for Discussion

- Considering how the dimensions of a box change when the volume is changed (doubled, halved, tripled)

Begin the discussion by asking students to list dimensions they found when doubling the number of cubes for the first three boxes in Activity 1C on *Student Activity Book* page 20 and to explain how they found the new dimensions. As students share dimensions, write them in a chart on the board or overhead.

Original Dimensions	Dimensions of New Box (double the volume)
2 × 6 × 4	2 × 12 × 4
	2 × 6 × 8
	1 × 6 × 16
	4 × 6 × 4
4 × 2 × 9	8 × 2 × 9
	4 × 2 × 18
	1 × 12 × 12
	4 × 4 × 9
4 × 5 × 6	4 × 10 × 6
	8 × 5 × 6
	4 × 5 × 12
	3 × 8 × 10

I asked you to think about a general strategy for finding dimensions for any box whose volume is doubled. What did you write?

For each student who explains, ask the following questions:

Will that work for any box? Are the new dimensions related to the original dimensions? How?

Students might say:

"Build two of the prisms, place them side by side in various ways, and figure out the dimensions."

"Double just one of the dimensions. If the dimensions are $4 \times 5 \times 6$, double one dimension: $4 \times 10 \times 6$ gives a box with double the volume."

Help students think about the relationship of the volume and how the dimensions change by asking these questions:

- When you tried to find a box with half the number of original cubes, what did you do?
- How did the strategy for doubling cubes help you think about this?

Most students have figured out that to double the volume, only one dimension needs to be doubled. If time permits, ask students to consider how the dimensions would change if we wanted to triple, or quadruple, the number of cubes—does the same thing hold true no matter how much the volume is increased?

3 SESSION FOLLOW-UP
Daily Practice and Homework

Daily Practice: For ongoing review, have students complete *Student Activity Book* page 24.

Homework: On *Student Activity Book* pages 25–26, students are given the dimension of a box and asked to find a new box (or boxes) that holds double the number of cubes as the original box. Make Three-Quarter-Inch Grid Paper (M11) available for students to take home.

Student Math Handbook: Students and families may use *Student Math Handbook* page 108 for reference and review. See pages 141–143 in the back of this unit.

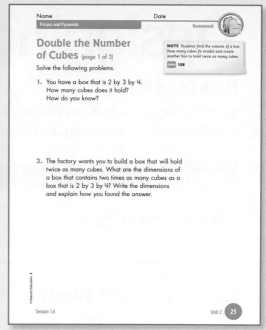

Name Date
Prisms and Pyramids
Homework

Double the Number of Cubes (page 1 of 2)

NOTE Students find the volume of a box (how many cubes fit inside) and create another box to hold twice as many cubes.
SMH 108

Solve the following problems.

1. You have a box that is 2 by 3 by 4. How many cubes does it hold? How do you know?

2. The factory wants you to build a box that will hold twice as many cubes. What are the dimensions of a box that contains two times as many cubes as a box that is 2 by 3 by 4? Write the dimensions and explain how you found the answer.

© Pearson Education 5

Session 1.6 Unit 2 25

▲ Student Activity Book, p. 25

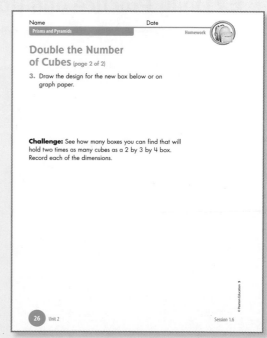

Name Date
Prisms and Pyramids
Homework

Double the Number of Cubes (page 2 of 2)

3. Draw the design for the new box below or on graph paper.

Challenge: See how many boxes you can find that will hold two times as many cubes as a 2 by 3 by 4 box. Record each of the dimensions.

© Pearson Education 5

26 Unit 2 Session 1.6

▲ Student Activity Book, p. 26

Designing Boxes

Math Focus Points

- Designing a box that can be completely filled with several different-shaped rectangular packages

Vocabulary

multiple

Today's Plan		Materials
1 ACTIVITY **Design a Box**	50 MIN PAIRS	• *Student Activity Book*, p. 27 • M11; M18 • Connecting cubes
2 DISCUSSION **Boxes That Work**	10 MIN CLASS	• *Student Activity Book*, p. 27
3 SESSION FOLLOW-UP **Daily Practice and Homework**		• *Student Activity Book*, pp. 28–30 • *Student Math Handbook*, pp. 105, 106–107

Ten-Minute Math

Quick Images: 3-D **Show Images 12–14 from *Quick Images: 3-D* (T27–T28) and follow the procedure for the basic routine. For each image, students discuss how they built their structures, including any revisions they made after each viewing. Ask students:**

- How did you remember the parts of the image?
- What did you notice about the relationship of the parts of the image?
- What helped you remember the whole image so that you could build your structure?

1 ACTIVITY
Design a Box

50 MIN PAIRS

The Packaging Factory has one final job for you. They would like to have one box that they can use to ship many different packages. The box needs to be a size and shape that can be completely filled by Packages A, B, C, or D. The box will be packed with only one type of package at a time. Each kind of package must fill the box to the top without leaving any gaps. Your job is to design and build the box.

Students work with a partner to complete *Student Activity Book* page 27. Allow students access to grid paper, connecting cubes, or whatever else they want to use to develop a design that works for all packages.❶

To solve the problem, students explore options for building structures to match the criteria.

By working with a partner, most students are able to come up with at least two boxes that work. Encourage all pairs to try to find more than two boxes that work.

ONGOING ASSESSMENT: Observing Students at Work

Students design a box that can be completely filled with each of four or five differently shaped packages.

- **How are students finding dimensions of a box?** Are they using different configurations of packages? Are they designing patterns for boxes? Are they using numbers and thinking about factors and multiples?❷
- **How do students test their answers?** Do they build the box and show how each type of package would fit?

Professional Development

❶ **Teacher Note:** Strategies for Designing Boxes, p. 121

Teaching Note

❷ **Using Multiples to Find the Answer** Some students use multiples to solve these problems. For example, for Package A to fill the box, all of the dimensions of the box must be multiples of 2. Packages B and D require that one dimension also be a multiple of 3. This is a useful strategy. If no student brings it up, you may want to ask whether thinking about factors and multiples helps determine dimensions. However, do not require students to use this strategy. It will make sense to some students but not to all.

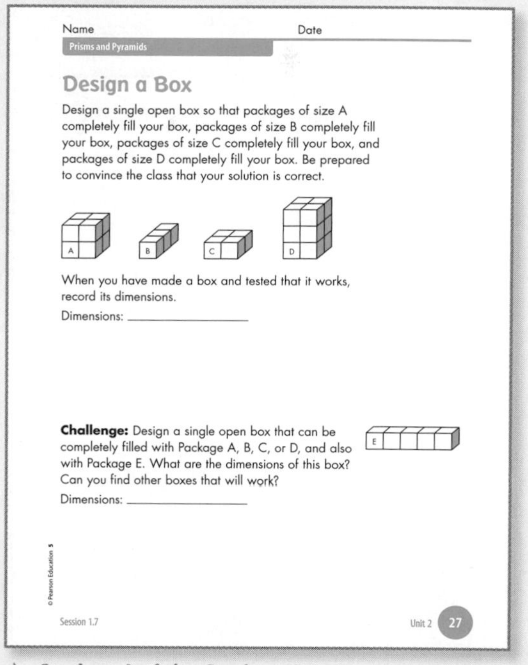

Name Date

Prisms and Pyramids

Design a Box

Design a single open box so that packages of size A completely fill your box, packages of size B completely fill your box, packages of size C completely fill your box, and packages of size D completely fill your box. Be prepared to convince the class that your solution is correct.

A B C D

When you have made a box and tested that it works, record its dimensions.

Dimensions: ______

Challenge: Design a single open box that can be completely filled with Package A, B, C, or D, and also with Package E. What are the dimensions of this box? Can you find other boxes that will work?

E

Dimensions: ______

© Pearson Education 5

Session 1.7 Unit 2 27

▲ Student Activity Book, p. 27

Name Date

Prisms and Pyramids

Daily Practice

Multiplication Starter Problems

NOTE Students practice flexibility with solving multiplication problems.

SMH 30–32

Solve each problem two ways, using the first steps listed below. Show your work clearly.

1. 49 × 25 = ______

Start by solving 50 × 25.	Start by solving 40 × 25.

2. 115 × 28 = ______

Start by solving 100 × 28.	Start by solving 115 × 10.

© Pearson Education 5

28 Unit 2 Session 1.7

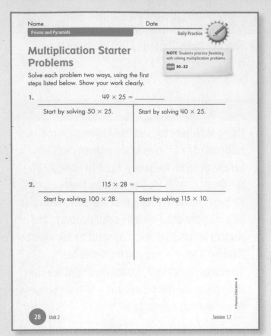

▲ Student Activity Book, p. 28

Name Date

Prisms and Pyramids

Homework

Solving Division Problems (page 1 of 2)

NOTE Students practice solving division problems.

SMH 38–39

Write a story problem that represents each division expression. Then solve the problem.

1. a. Write a story problem that represents 528 ÷ 24.

b. Solve 528 ÷ 24. Show your solution clearly.

© Pearson Education 5

Session 1.7 Unit 2 29

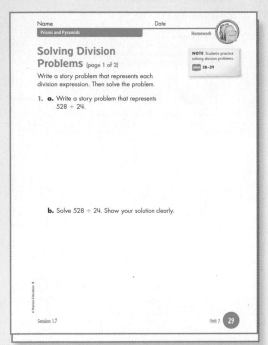

▲ Student Activity Book, pp. 29–30

DIFFERENTIATION: Supporting the Range of Learners

Extension Challenge students who easily find dimensions for Packages A–D to find dimensions that also fit Package E.

DISCUSSION

10 MIN CLASS

2 Boxes That Work

Math Focus Points for Discussion

- Designing a box that can be completely filled with several differently shaped rectangular packages

Have pairs of students tell the class the dimensions they found for a box for Packages A, B, C and D and explain how they solved the problem. For each pair that shares the dimensions they found, ask questions such as these:

- Do we all agree that the dimensions work?
- Who has questions for [Margaret]?
- Who else got the same dimensions?
- Did you solve it the same way?
- Who got a different answer?

SESSION FOLLOW-UP

3 Daily Practice and Homework

Daily Practice: For ongoing review, have students complete *Student Activity Book* page 28.

Homework: Students practice solving division problems on *Student Activity Book* pages 29–30.

Student Math Handbook: Students and families may use *Student Math Handbook* pages 105, 106–107 for reference and review. See pages 141–143 in the back of this unit.

INVESTIGATION 2

Mathematical Emphasis

Volume Structuring rectangular prisms and determining their volume

Math Focus Points

- Determining the volume, in cubic centimeters, of a small prism
- Constructing units of volume—cubic centimeter, cubic inch, cubic foot, cubic yard (optional), cubic meter
- Choosing an appropriate unit of volume to measure a large space
- Finding the volume of a large space, such as the classroom, using cubic meters
- Considering how the dimensions of a box change when the volume is changed (doubled, halved, or tripled)

This Investigation also focuses on

- Describing and defending measurement methods

Using Standard Cubic Units

	Student Activity Book	Student Math Handbook	Professional Development: Read Ahead of Time
SESSION 2.1 p. 64 **Finding Cubic Centimeters** Students determine the number of cubic centimeters that fill an unmarked, closed box that measures 5 x 8 x 4 centimeters. They discuss different units of volume.	31–32	109–110	
SESSION 2.2 p. 71 **Building Models of Volume Units** Students build 4 or 5 standard units of volume. They discuss which unit of volume would be appropriate for measuring the space in their classroom and develop a plan for measuring that space.	33–34	109–110	• **Dialogue Box:** Talking About Units of Volume, p. 137 • **Dialogue Box:** Choosing a Volume Unit to Measure the Classroom, p. 138
SESSION 2.3 p. 77 **The Space Inside Our Classroom** Students determine the number of cubic meters that fit in their classroom, describing and justifying their measurement methods and discussing discrepancies.	35	105, 106–107	• **Teacher Note:** Strategies for Measuring Space in the Classroom, p. 123
SESSION 2.4 p. 83 **Assessment: Measuring Volume in Cubic Centimeters** In a Math Workshop, students are given the dimensions of a box in centimeters. They then find two boxes that hold double the number of centimeter cubes as the original and two boxes that hold half. Students are assessed on measuring the volume of an unmarked box in cubic centimeters.	36–38	106–107, 108	

Ten-Minute Math See page 16 for an overview.

Estimation and Number Sense

- M13–M15, Digit Cards

Materials to Gather	Materials to Prepare
• **Scissors** (1 set per pair) • **Tape** (1 roll per pair) • **Centimeter cubes** (20 per pair) • **Centimeter rulers** (1 per pair) • **Calculators** (as needed) • **Inch cube** • **12-inch ruler**	• **M22, Pattern for a Closed Box** Make copies. (1 per pair of students and 1 for teacher) • **M18, Centimeter Grid Paper** Make copies for use throughout this Investigation. • **5 cm x 8 cm x 4 cm Closed Box** (from copy of M22) Cut out and tape together a demonstration box. • **Chart paper** Make a 3-column chart titled "Units of Measurement." Title the first column "Units of Length," the second "Units of Weight," and the third "Units of Volume."
• **M18, Centimeter Grid Paper** (as needed) • **Metersticks** (as needed) • **Yardsticks** (optional) • **12-inch rulers** (as needed) • **Masking tape** (1 roll per 4 students) • **Scissors** (1 per pair) • **Tape** (1 per pair)	• **M23** Make copies. (as needed)
• **Connecting cubes** (as needed) • **Cubic meter** (constructed in Session 2.2) • **Metersticks** (1 per pair)	• **M11, Three-Quarter-Inch Grid Paper** Make copies. (as needed; optional) • **String or paper strips cut in one-meter lengths** If you do not have enough metersticks available for each pair of students, prepare 1-meter lengths of string or paper strips. (as needed)
• **M18, Centimeter Grid Paper** (as needed) • **Centimeter cubes** (10 per student) • **Centimeter rulers** (1 per student) • **Calculators** (as needed) • **Scissors** (1 per student)	• **M24, Assessment: Measuring Volume in Cubic Centimeters** Make copies. (1 per student) • **M25, Assessment Checklist: Measuring Volume in Cubic Centimeters** Make copies. (1 per 6 students) ✓

✓ Checklist Available

Finding Cubic Centimeters

Math Focus Points

- Determining the volume, in cubic centimeters, of a small prism

Vocabulary

cubic centimeter
volume
linear

Today's Plan		Materials
ACTIVITY 1 **Finding Cubic Centimeters**	30 MIN PAIRS	• M22*; M18* • 5 cm x 8 cm x 4 cm closed box*; scissors; tape; centimeter cubes; centimeter rulers; calculators
DISCUSSION 2 **How Many Cubic Centimeters?**	20 MIN CLASS	
DISCUSSION 3 **Introducing Volume Units**	10 MIN CLASS	• Chart: "Units of Measurement"*; centimeter cube; centimeter ruler; inch cube; 12-inch ruler
SESSION FOLLOW-UP 4 **Daily Practice and Homework**		• *Student Activity Book*, pp. 31–32 • *Student Math Handbook*, pp. 109–110

*See *Materials to Prepare*, p. 63.

Ten-Minute Math

Estimation and Number Sense Using Digit Cards, create two 2-digit by 2-digit *multiplication* problems, (___ × ___). Give students 30 seconds to mentally estimate a product that is as close as possible to the exact answer. Students may jot down partial products if they wish. Some students may be able to determine the exact answer. Have two or three students explain their work, and record these strategies on the board or overhead.

ACTIVITY 1

30 MIN PAIRS

Finding Cubic Centimeters

Show a centimeter cube to the class.

This cube measures one centimeter along each edge. It is called a cubic centimeter. Today you're going to figure out how many cubic centimeters it takes to completely fill this *closed* box that you'll cut out and tape together from this pattern. [Hold up Pattern for a Closed Box cut out from M22.]

Show the closed box you prepared, but *do not* tell students the dimensions of the box (5 cm x 8 cm x 4 cm).

Because we don't have a large supply of centimeter cubes, even if this box were open, as a class you would not all have enough to fill the whole box or even the bottom layer. Therefore, you need to come up with some measuring strategies that don't depend on having many cubes. You can use centimeter rulers and calculators to help you. When you have an answer, write it down. Then we'll talk together about what you have found.

Have students work in pairs to cut out and tape the box together. Have centimeter rulers, centimeter cubes, and calculators available for their use as needed to solve the problem.[1]

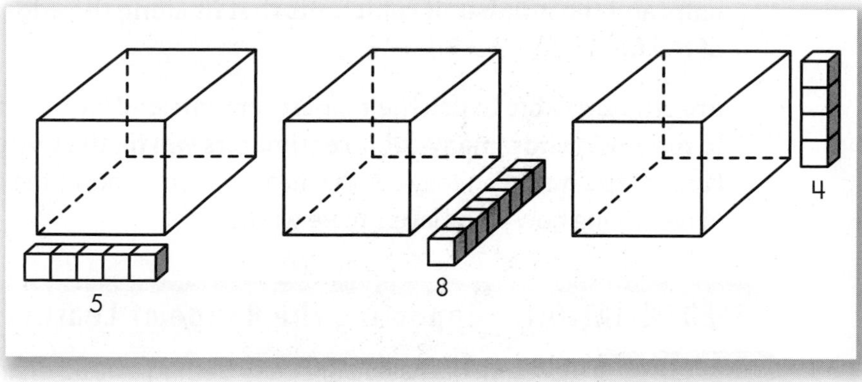

Math Note

[1] **Relating Cubic Units to Linear Units** In this Investigation, students learn to relate units of cubic measurement to units of linear measurement as they recognize that the lengths of the edges of cubic units are commonly used units of length. For example, the length of the edge of a cubic centimeter is a centimeter, the length of the edge of a cubic yard is a yard, and so on. Therefore, measuring the dimensions of the box in *linear* units indicates the number of *cubic* units that fit along the edges of the box. For example, as students measure the dimensions of the paper box as 5, 4, and 8 centimeters, some will understand that this means that 5 cubic centimeters fit along the bottom front edge, 4 cubic centimeters fit along the right vertical edge, and 8 cubic centimeters fit along the depth. Students who do not yet see this relationship will develop this understanding as they work on the activities of this Investigation.

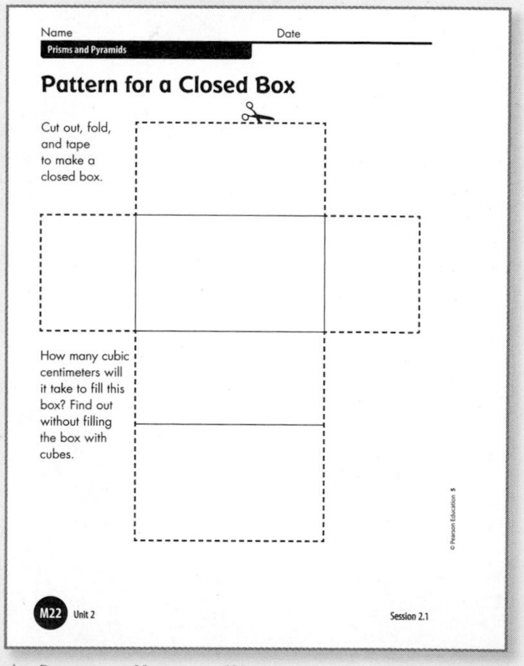

Name Date

Prisms and Pyramids

Pattern for a Closed Box

Cut out, fold, and tape to make a closed box.

How many cubic centimeters will it take to fill this box? Find out without filling the box with cubes.

© Pearson Education 5

M22 Unit 2 Session 2.1

▲ Resource Masters, M22

As students work, move from pair to pair and observe their strategies. If students have measured the dimensions, ask them why they did so. If they do not specifically say they measured the dimensions to find out how many cubes fit along each edge, point to an edge of the box and ask them this:

You said that this edge measured 5 centimeters. How many cubes will fit along this edge of the box?

Their answers will tell you whether they understand the significance of their ruler measurement. If students do not appear to understand this relationship, ask them to place cubes along that edge of the box and ask what they notice about the measurement in centimeters and the number of cubes that fit along that edge.

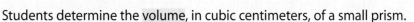

ONGOING ASSESSMENT: Observing Students at Work

Students determine the volume, in cubic centimeters, of a small prism.

- **What strategies do students use to determine the number of centimeter cubes that will fill the box?** Do they measure the dimensions of the box with the centimeter ruler? Do they place cubes outside the box along each edge?
- **Do students demonstrate understanding of the relationship between measuring the dimensions of the box in linear units and the number of cubic units that fit along the edges of the box?**
- **Are students able to use their measurements and/or the cubes to determine how many cubic centimeters will fill the bottom layer of the box?** Can they use the measurements and/or the cubes to determine how many layers there will be?

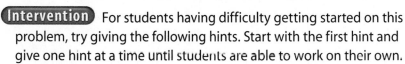

DIFFERENTIATION: Supporting the Range of Learners

Intervention For students having difficulty getting started on this problem, try giving the following hints. Start with the first hint and give one hint at a time until students are able to work on their own.

- Could using a ruler help you?
- What if you measure the edges of the box—will that help?
- What if you mark centimeters off at the edges? [You may have to illustrate this for students.]

- [Show a cube.] Here is a cubic centimeter. Can you use it to help you?
- [Point to one edge of the box.] How many cubes fit along this edge?
- [Offer a copy of Centimeter Grid Paper (M18).] Does it help if you make the box from this paper?

These questions help students understand that measuring the dimensions of the box in linear units indicates the number of cubic units that fit along the edges of the box.

DISCUSSION

20 MIN CLASS

2 How Many Cubic Centimeters?

Math Focus Points for Discussion

- Determining the volume, in cubic centimeters, of a small prism

When most students have found a solution, call them together to share their strategies for determining the number of cubic centimeters that fit in the closed box. Students may place cubes along the edges to determine the dimensions or they may measure the dimensions of the box. Ask several pairs of students who used different strategies to share their solutions.

I noticed that [Alex] and [Renaldo] used centimeter cubes to help them solve this problem. Can you tell us what you did?

[Mercedes], I noticed that you and [Janet] used your centimeter ruler to measure the dimensions of the box. How did knowing the dimensions help you find the number of cubic centimeters that fit inside the box?

Students might say:

"We put centimeter cubes outside each edge of the box. We figured out that the box fit 5 cubes across and 8 cubes back. That's five rows of 8 cubes, so we knew that the bottom of the box would hold 40 cubes. The box is 4 cubes high, so that told us that there are four layers of 40. That means that there are 160 cubes in all."

"We did sort of the same thing, but we didn't use cubes. We measured the box and figured out that the bottom is 5 centimeters by 8 centimeters, so we knew that the bottom layer would have 40 cubes. The box is 4 centimeters high, so we multiplied 40 times 4 because there are 4 layers. We got 160 for our answer, too."

To help students connect the two strategies, ask them to explain what is similar about the two ways of solving this problem.

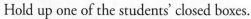

DISCUSSION

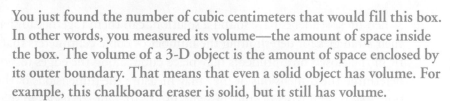

3 Introducing Volume Units

10 MIN CLASS

Hold up one of the students' closed boxes.

You just found the number of cubic centimeters that would fill this box. In other words, you measured its volume—the amount of space inside the box. The volume of a 3-D object is the amount of space enclosed by its outer boundary. That means that even a solid object has volume. For example, this chalkboard eraser is solid, but it still has volume.

Direct students' attention to the "Units of Measurement" chart that you prepared.

When we measure, we use different kinds of units depending on what we are measuring. What are some units we use to measure length? (meters, centimeters, millimeters, kilometers, inches, feet, yards, miles) What are some units we use to measure weight? (kilograms, grams, ounces, pounds, tons)

Record students' responses in the appropriate columns on the chart.

Just as we have special units to measure length and weight, we also have special units to measure volume. [Hold up a centimeter cube.] You figured out that it would take 160 centimeter cubes like this one to fill the box we worked on in our last activity. Therefore, we can say that the volume of the box is 160 cubic centimeters.

One way we can write cubic centimeters is "cm^3." The little 3 means "cubed"—this is because we're multiplying centimeters times centimeters times centimeters.

As you continue the discussion of different types of units for measuring volume, write both the words and this "shorthand" notation on the board (e.g., cubic meters, m^3).

Students make connections between units of measuring length and units of measuring volume.

Write *cubic centimeters* on the chart under the heading "Units of Volume."

What are some other units that we could use to measure volume?

List students' ideas on the chart, or help them by suggesting units such as cubic meters, cubic inches, cubic feet, and cubic yards.

What do you notice about the names of each of these volume units? What do they have in common?

Students are likely to comment that each of the units begins with the word *cubic* followed by a unit of linear measurement. To help students understand the reason for this, display the centimeter cube once again.

Remember that we can call this a centimeter cube *or* a cubic centimeter. *Cubic* is a way of identifying that the unit of measure is a cube. Why do you think we call this unit a cubic *centimeter* as opposed to a cubic *inch* or a cubic *foot?*

Name Date

Prisms and Pyramids Daily Practice

Factors of 120 and 210

Find all the ways to multiply to make each product, using whole numbers. First, find the ways with two numbers, and then find ways to multiply with more than two numbers.

NOTE Students practice finding multiplication expressions with two numbers and with more than two numbers for 120 and 210.

SMH 33–34

1. Multiplying to make 120

Ways to multiply with two numbers: Example: 12×10	Ways to multiply with more than two numbers: Example: $2 \times 6 \times 10$

2. Multiplying to make 210

Ways to multiply with two numbers:	Ways to multiply with more than two numbers:

Session 2.1 Unit 2 31

▲ Student Activity Book, p. 31

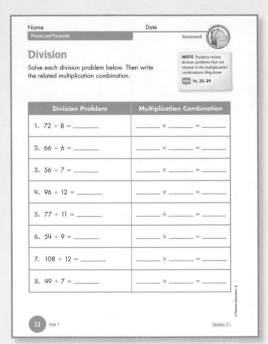

Name Date

Prisms and Pyramids Homework

Division

Solve each division problem below. Then write the related multiplication combination.

NOTE Students review division problems that are related to the multiplication combinations they know.

SMH 14, 25–29

Division Problem	Multiplication Combination
1. $72 \div 8 =$ ______	______ × ______ = ______
2. $66 \div 6 =$ ______	______ × ______ = ______
3. $56 \div 7 =$ ______	______ × ______ = ______
4. $96 \div 12 =$ ______	______ × ______ = ______
5. $77 \div 11 =$ ______	______ × ______ = ______
6. $54 \div 9 =$ ______	______ × ______ = ______
7. $108 \div 12 =$ ______	______ × ______ = ______
8. $49 \div 7 =$ ______	______ × ______ = ______

32 Unit 7 Session 2.1

▲ Student Activity Book, p. 32

Students should understand that the use of *centimeter* in this volume unit refers to the length of the edges of the cube. Demonstrate this by comparing (or asking a student to compare) a centimeter length on a ruler with a centimeter cube.

If a cubic centimeter is a cube that measures one centimeter at each edge, how long are the edges of a cubic inch? A cubic yard? A cubic foot?

Once again, demonstrate this relationship by comparing an inch on a ruler with a one-inch cube. Then, let students know that they will build common volume units in the next session.

4

SESSION FOLLOW-UP
Daily Practice and Homework

Daily Practice: For ongoing review, have students complete *Student Activity Book* page 31.

Homework: Students review division problems that are related to the multiplication combinations they know on *Student Activity Book* page 32.

Student Math Handbook: Students and families may use *Student Math Handbook* pages 109–110 for reference and review. See pages 141–143 in the back of this unit.

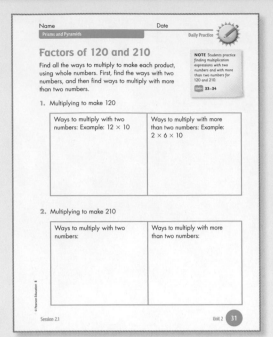

Building Models of Volume Units

Math Focus Points

- Constructing units of volume—cubic centimeter, cubic inch, cubic foot, cubic yard (optional), cubic meter
- Choosing an appropriate unit of volume to measure a large space

Vocabulary

cubic meter

Today's Plan		Materials
1 ACTIVITY **Building Models of Volume Units**	30 MIN PAIRS GROUPS	• M18*; M23* • Metersticks; yardsticks; 12-inch rulers; masking tape; scissors; tape
2 DISCUSSION **Which Unit Should We Use?**	15 MIN CLASS	• Models of volume units (from Activity 1)
3 ACTIVITY **A Plan to Measure Classroom Space**	15 MIN PAIRS	
4 SESSION FOLLOW-UP **Daily Practice and Homework**		• *Student Activity Book,* pp. 33–34 • *Student Math Handbook,* pp. 109–110

*See *Materials to Prepare,* p. 63.

Ten-Minute Math

Estimation and Number Sense Using Digit Cards, create two 2-digit by 2-digit *multiplication* problems, (__ __ × __ __). Give students 30 seconds to mentally estimate a product that is as close as possible to the exact answer. Students may jot down partial products if they wish. Some students may be able to determine the exact answer. Have two or three students explain their work, and record these strategies on the board or overhead.

Teaching Note

1 Why Not Build a Cubic Yard? Because the size of a cubic yard is fairly close to the size of a cubic meter (and because not all classrooms will have enough yardsticks and metersticks), students are only asked to build the cubic meter. If you have yardsticks and want students to see the relationship of a cubic inch, cubic foot, and cubic yard, consider having a group of students also build a cubic yard.

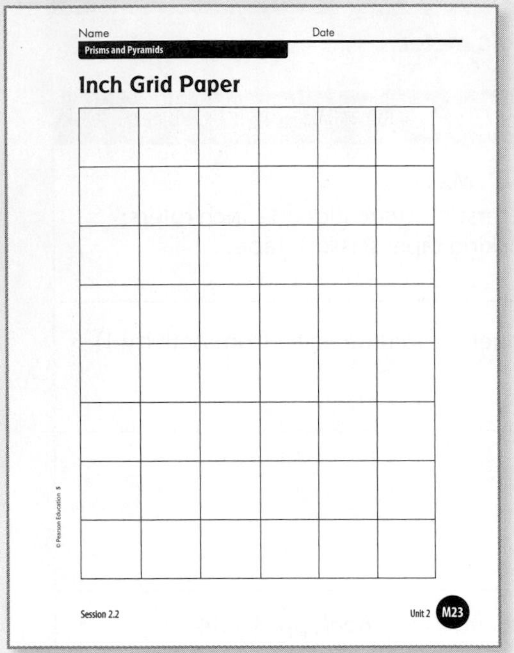
Name Date
Prisms and Pyramids
Inch Grid Paper
Session 2.2
Unit 2 M23

▲ Resource Masters, M23; T33

ACTIVITY

30 MIN PAIRS GROUPS

1 Building Models of Volume Units

In the next session, you are going to measure the space inside this classroom. In other words, you'll find its volume. Before you measure the classroom, you need to decide what units of measure are the best to use. So today, you'll work in pairs or small groups to build some standard units for measuring volume—cubic inches, cubic centimeters, cubic feet, and cubic meters.

You may have students build cubic yards, as well. 1

Each group or pair will build one of the standard units. When all the units are built, we'll look at them together and discuss why some units would work better than others for measuring this large space.

Group students according to how many materials you have available for the different units. For building cubic meters and cubic yards (if they are doing so), plan on groups of 4 for each unit because it takes this many students to hold the metersticks or yardsticks in place while they are being taped.

Students build a cubic meter by using 12 metersticks, joined at the corners with plenty of masking tape. If you have more wall space than metersticks, students can create a model of a cubic meter by marking out a square meter on the floor with masking tape and another square meter in masking tape on the adjacent wall. Adding 5 metersticks for the top and outside edges will complete the model. If your room has an available corner, the same plan can work with only 3 metersticks.

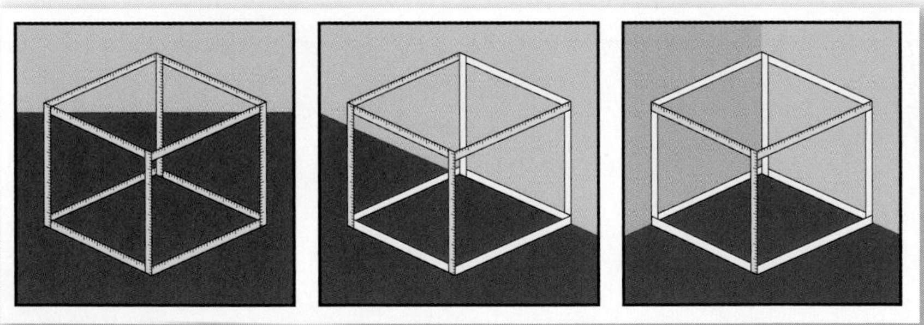

Assign groups of two to four to build cubic feet units by using rulers, following the same procedure as for metersticks. All remaining students work in pairs to make cubic inches and cubic centimeters with grid paper, scissors, and tape.

Follow the same procedure for building a cubic yard (optional). Keep at least one of the cubic meter units for use in the next session.

ONGOING ASSESSMENT: Observing Students at Work

Students build standard units of volume.

- **Are students able to build the cubic units?** If not, what is confusing them? Is it the structure of the cube? Do they find it difficult to tape the different parts together?

DISCUSSION

2 Which Unit Should We Use?

15 MIN CLASS

Math Focus Points for Discussion

- Choosing an appropriate unit of volume to measure a large space

After students have finished building their models, display the units where everyone can see and compare them.

By observing various models of cubic units, students gain a firm grasp of the characteristics that make a cubic unit and enhance their understanding of volume.

- What do you notice about each of these units? How are they the same? How are they different?
- Which is the smallest volume unit that we built? Which is the largest?❷

Students are likely to comment on the fact that each of the units is a cube but that they differ in size, with the cubic centimeter being the smallest and the cubic meter being the largest. If students do not bring up the characteristics that make each unit a cube, bring up this question yourself.

Differentiation

❷ **English Language Learners** In this activity, students need to be comfortable discussing various units of measure. You may want to meet with English Language Learners ahead of time to give them a chance to practice expressing their ideas. Use visual aids that represent units of measure to provide concrete examples. Let's say that I want to measure the volume of this box. I have some different units of measure: a ruler, a meterstick, and a five-inch strip of paper. What do you notice about each of these units? How are they similar? How are they different? Which unit is the smallest? Which unit is the largest? This preparation will help English Language Learners participate more fully in the class discussion.

Remind students that in the next session, they will measure the space inside their entire classroom.❸

Now that you've built and compared these units of volume, think about which units would be good to use to measure the space inside this classroom. It may help to think about which units would be hardest to use and which would be easiest. Talk to a partner about this question and be ready to explain your thinking.

Give students a few minutes to talk about this question. Then call them back together to share their thinking. Students may want to talk about their ideas for how to find the number of units in the classroom. Although they may need to do some of this in order to explain their ideas about which units are most efficient for measuring a large space, limit such discussion because pairs will devise their own plans for measuring the classroom in the next activity.

Students should recognize that measuring with a larger unit is more manageable; the numbers stay smaller and the actual measuring is easier. If these ideas are not expressed, raise it yourself.❹

Suppose that we measured first with a small unit—such as cubic centimeters—and then a bigger unit such as cubic meters. How would the number we get for the amount of space in the room be different? Are there more cubic centimeters or cubic meters in the classroom? Why?

Cubic feet, cubic yards, and cubic meters are all good sizes for measuring the classroom. However, because we want to compare the results when everyone has finished measuring, it's important for each pair to use the same unit. So for this activity, you will use cubic meters to measure.

Save at least one of the cubic meter units that students constructed so that students can refer to it during the next session as they measure the classroom, and then discuss how many cubic meters they found.

3 ACTIVITY

15 MIN PAIRS

A Plan to Measure Classroom Space

In the next session, students will extend the schemes they developed with small cubes and boxes to determine the amount of space in—or volume of—their classroom. To solve this problem meaningfully, students first need to mentally construct cubic meters and visualize how these units fill the classroom. Help students connect the work they have done finding the volume of rectangular prisms in previous sessions to the work of measuring the classroom.❺

Professional Development

❸ **Dialogue Box:** Talking About Units of Volume, p. 137

❹ **Dialogue Box:** Choosing a Volume Unit to Measure the Classroom, p. 138

Teaching Note

❺ **Making the Problem Manageable** If your classroom is not a rectangular prism, make the problem manageable by specifying some part of it that is. Additionally, to simplify the calculations, have students round to the nearest whole meter.

Imagine that our classroom is completely empty—no desks or chairs or shelves, just the floor and walls and the ceiling. When you think about the space inside the entire classroom, it may be helpful to think about how much space for air there is in the empty classroom. You can also think of the empty classroom as a large "box" that can be filled completely with cubic meters.

Your task right now is to make a plan for measuring the amount of space in that large "box" that is our classroom. Your plan should work for any room, just as your strategies for finding the number of cubes to fill a small box will work for any box.

Because we are going to use cubic meters as our unit of volume, the problem is to find how many cubic meters fit in our classroom. Keep in mind that you'll have metersticks, one-meter lengths of string, one-meter lengths of paper, and calculators available for use, so you can include them in your plan.

Initially, some students may not focus on volume. They may take the area of the floor instead of the volume to quantify the space in the room. Although this is not the point of the activity, it is consistent with everyday conceptions of the size of the room. For example, for real estate and architecture purposes, the size of the house is usually given in terms of the total area of its floor in square feet. Often, when we think about the amount of space in a room, we are really wondering how many people or things will fit on the floor. If you find students thinking in terms of floor area, emphasize finding the amount of space for air in the room.

If many students are thinking about area instead of "space for air," discuss this as a whole class. If necessary, compare the model cubic meters with a square meter (laid out, for example, in masking tape) and with a meterstick. Ask students to think about the different things these three different units (meter, square meter, cubic meter) can measure.

Working in pairs, students write their plans for measuring the volume of the classroom. In the next session, they implement their plan and compare their results with those of other students. 6

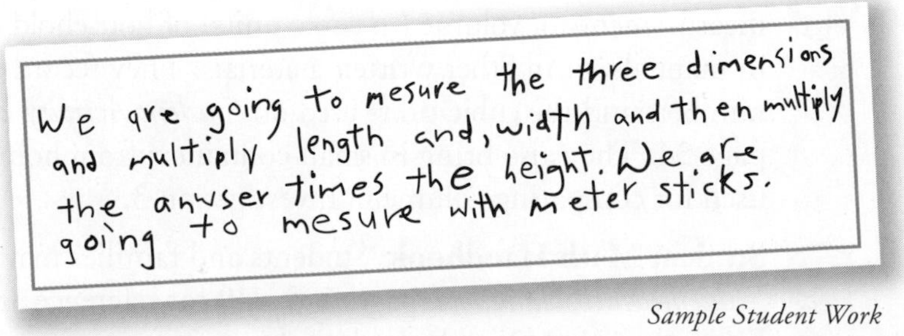
We are going to mesure the three dimensions and multiply length and, width and then multiply the anwser times the height. We are going to mesure with meter sticks.

Sample Student Work

Teaching Note

6 **Making Plans Explicit and Dealing with Incomplete Thinking** As students work on this activity, ask questions to help them make their plans explicit (e.g., what they plan to measure, what measurement tools they intend to use, and how they will use their measurements to determine the volume of the classroom). It is important to recognize, however, that their plans may include mistakes. Although your questions may help students recognize and correct some mistakes, do not expect or insist that they correct them all while they make their plans. Discovering mistakes themselves as they start the actual measuring in Session 2.3 will result in a deeper understanding of volume.

Name Date

Prisms and Pyramids Daily Practice

Large and Small Hunt

In each row, circle the largest product or quotient. Then underline the smallest.

NOTE Students estimate the answers to multiplication and division problems.

SMH 30–32, 38–39

1.	46 × 77	67 × 51	39 × 86
2.	23 × 97	36 × 58	69 × 33
3.	468 ÷ 26	68 ÷ 34	114 ÷ 6
4.	225 ÷ 15	905 ÷ 5	224 ÷ 16

Ongoing Review

5. Which multiplication fact is related to 72 ÷ 9 = 8?

A. 8 × 9 = 72 **C.** 7 × 10 = 70

B. 72 ÷ 8 = 9 **D.** 80 ÷ 8 = 10

Session 2.2 Unit 2 33

▲ Student Activity Book, p. 33

Name Date

Prisms and Pyramids Homework

Measurements of Volume

NOTE Students, with the aid of an adult/adults, find volumes for common household items.

SMH 109–110

Look in and around your home for any recorded measurements of volume. Look on household items (refrigerators and freezers), in manuals, on other written materials (a water bill), or on any item that might have a measurement of volume recorded on it (the trunk space of a car).

Record any measurements that are given in **cubic** units. Write down both the **number** of cubic units and the **kind** of cubic units used.

This Is Where My Measurement Was Found	Number of Cubic Units	Kind of Cubic Units

Containers from Home

We will soon be comparing the volumes of different household containers. Please find 3 or 4 clean, empty containers at home to bring to school. The recycling bin is a good place to look.

The containers should have sealed edges with no small openings so that sand does not leak out. As a guideline for size, the containers should fit together comfortably in a paper lunch bag.

34 Unit 2 Session 2.2

▲ Student Activity Book, p. 34

measure a cube Then take cubes and measure from the floor to the ceiling Keep the number and Then measure from East to West. Then measure from North to South Multiply them all and then you will find out how many cubes would fit in the classroom.

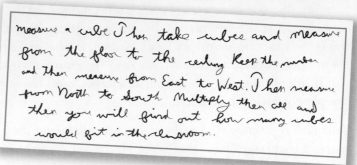

Sample Student Work

ONGOING ASSESSMENT: Observing Students at Work

Students use understanding of the structure of rectangular prisms to make plans for finding the volume of their classroom.

- **How do students' plans indicate the ways they are thinking about finding volume?** Do they relate the work they did finding the volume of a small prism to finding the volume of the classroom (e.g., finding the number of cubic units that will cover the floor [bottom layer] and then determining how many layers there are)?
- **Do students' plans involve finding the three dimensions of the room?** What measurement tools do they plan to use? Do they demonstrate understanding that when they have linear measurements, they multiply them together to find the volume?
- **Do students' plans demonstrate understanding that they are finding the volume in cubic meters?**

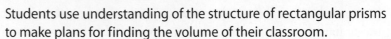

4 SESSION FOLLOW-UP
Daily Practice and Homework

Daily Practice: For ongoing review, have students complete *Student Activity Book* page 33.

Homework: With family help, students find recorded measurements of volume (in cubic units) of household items, in manuals, or in other written materials. They record both the numbers and the cubic units used on *Student Activity Book* page 34. They also bring in small containers from home to be used for comparing volume in Investigation 3.

Student Math Handbook: Students and families may use *Student Math Handbook* pages 109–110 for reference and review. See pages 141–143 in the back of this unit.

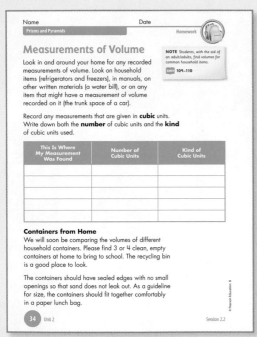

The Space Inside Our Classroom

Math Focus Points

- Finding the volume of a large space, such as the classroom, using cubic meters
- Describing and defending measurement methods

Vocabulary

length
width
height

Today's Plan		Materials
1 ACTIVITY **How Many Cubic Meters in Our Classroom?**	40 MIN PAIRS	• M11 (optional) • Cubic meter (constructed in Session 2.2); metersticks or string or paper strips cut in 1-meter lengths*; connecting cubes
2 DISCUSSION **How We Measured**	20 MIN CLASS	
3 SESSION FOLLOW-UP **Daily Practice**		• *Student Activity Book*, p. 35 • *Student Math Handbook*, pp. 105, 106–107

*See *Materials to Prepare*, p. 63.

Ten-Minute Math

Estimation and Number Sense Using Digit Cards, create two 3-digit by 2-digit division problems, (___ ___ ___ ÷ ___ ___). Give students 30 seconds to mentally estimate a quotient as close as possible to the exact answer. Students may jot down partial quotients or products if they wish. Some students may be able to determine the exact answer. Have two or three students explain their work, and record these strategies on the board or overhead.

Teaching Note

➊ **Dealing with Physical Obstacles in the Classroom** Furniture and other physical obstacles (such as figuring out how to measure the height of the room) can pose problems for students as they attempt to measure the dimensions of the room. Help them find a way to deal with these problems. For example, one pair of students was trying to measure the length of a wall along the floor and was stumped by a short bookcase in the way. Until the teacher asked them about it, the pair did not see that they could measure along the wall above the bookcase to find the same length. Also help students figure out ways to safely measure the height of the room.

ACTIVITY 1

40 MIN PAIRS

How Many Cubic Meters in Our Classroom?

Before starting this session, out of the sight of your students, measure the dimensions and find the volume of your classroom in cubic meters. This way you will be able to judge the accuracy of students' answers.

We are trying to find out how much space for air there is in our classroom. Yesterday, we decided to do this by using cubic meters as our unit of volume, and you each worked on your plan. Let's begin today by making some estimates. How many cubic meters do you think will fit inside our classroom? Why?

Ask several students to share their estimates and their strategies for making them. Then introduce the activity.

Today, you will carry out your plans to find the number of cubic meters that fit in the classroom. You and your partner should record your answer to this problem and explain how you found this answer. You must be able to convince your classmates that your answer and the method you used are correct.

Student pairs who planned together continue to work together as they determine the amount of space in the classroom in cubic meters. Remind them to round their measurements to the nearest whole meter. Thus, if they first measure the length of the classroom, that measurement should be rounded to the nearest meter. As students come up with answers, they can check with other pairs. If pairs have different answers, they should determine why.➊

Students try out various strategies to find the volume of the classroom.

As students are working, ask questions that help them elaborate and justify their ideas. For example, if they decide to measure the room in meters and multiply these dimensions, ask questions to ensure that they understand what they are doing.❷

- What does your unit for measuring space look like?
- You measured in meters, but you got an answer in cubic meters. How does that work?
- When you measured, you found that the length of the room was 8 meters. What does that tell you about how many cubic meters will fit along the length of the room?

ONGOING ASSESSMENT: Observing Students at Work

Students determine the volume of their classroom in cubic meters.

- **If students recognize mistakes in their plans, are they able to correct them?**
- **Are students able to relate their linear measurements to the number of cubic meters that will fit along an edge of the classroom?** If they measure the length of the room as 10 meters, do they understand that 10 cubic meters will fit along that length?
- **After students have determined the dimensions of the room, do they multiply them to find the volume?**
- **Do they recognize that their answers must be expressed in *cubic* units (cubic meters)?**
- **How do students articulate their methods for determining volume?** Are their explanations clear? Are they able to justify their methods?

DIFFERENTIATION: Supporting the Range of Learners

Intervention Students having difficulty with this activity may benefit by modeling the situation with connecting cubes or paper boxes. They could make a scale model classroom, either as a paper box made from copies of Three-Quarter-Inch Grid Paper (M11) or as a solid package of cubes, each cube representing a cubic meter. Thus, if the room measures 10 meters x 8 meters on the floor and is 3 meters high, students would make a box or package that measures 10 x 8 x 3 cubes. This model should help students better visualize how cubic meters fit into the classroom.

Professional Development

❷ **Teacher Note:** Strategies for Measuring Space in the Classroom, p. 123

If students are still having difficulty, suggest that they work first on a simpler problem. For example, how many cubic feet would fit in a box the size of your desk? This reduces the scale of the problem, making it easier to relate to their earlier work with small cubes and paper boxes. Ask questions that encourage students to relate the ways they found volume on a small scale in previous sessions to how they might find the amount of space in large-scale environments.

- How did you find the number of cubes in a box?
- Does that strategy help here (for finding the amount of space in a room)?

DISCUSSION

2 How We Measured

20 MIN CLASS

Math Focus Points for Discussion

- Finding the volume of a large space, the classroom, using cubic meters
- Describing and defending measurement methods

Start the discussion by asking questions that encourage students to review and clarify the problem that was posed. It is important to refocus students' attention repeatedly on visualizing what is happening as they measure space. When necessary, direct their attention to a cubic meter (constructed in Session 2.2) that is on display.

- What was the problem you were trying to solve? *(What is the number of cubic meters in the classroom?)*
- What exactly does this number tell us? *(how much space or volume our classroom has)*
- When you say that there are 240 cubic meters in the classroom, what does that mean? *(that 240 cubes like the one built from the metersticks and tape could be put in our classroom)*

After reviewing the problem, students report their numerical answers. As they report, record the numbers on a line plot on the board.

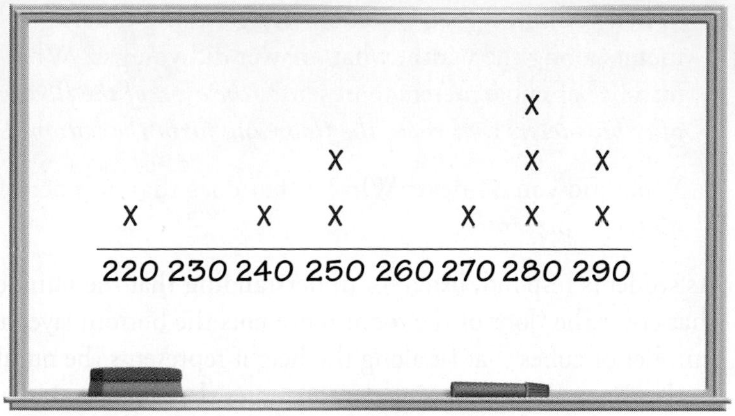

Ask pairs with different answers to explain and justify their solutions. Answers will differ because of computational errors, incorrect methods, or errors in measuring the dimensions of the classroom. Help students see the different sources of their errors as they listen to one another's explanations and justifications of answers and methods.

These two pairs both measured the room's **length**, **width**, and **height**. Then, they multiplied these numbers together. So how could they have different answers?

Finally, ask students to explain the different methods they used, both in measuring and in doing the computation. Encourage them to elaborate on what kinds of measurement they used and why.

- What parts of the room did you measure? Why?
- How did you find the number of cubic meters that fit along this edge of the floor?
- Some people measured one edge of the floor with a meter tape. What did they learn from that?

Make sure that students also describe and justify any computations they did.

[Tamira], you said that you and [Avery] multiplied to get your answer. What numbers did you multiply? Why?

Some students may say that they multiplied the three dimensions (length, width, and height) because that is the method they discovered for finding the number of cubes that fit in paper boxes. Other students may say that they determined how many cubic meters fit along the length and along the width of the room (on the floor) and then multiplied these numbers together. They then multiplied that number by the number of cubic meters that fit along the height of the room.

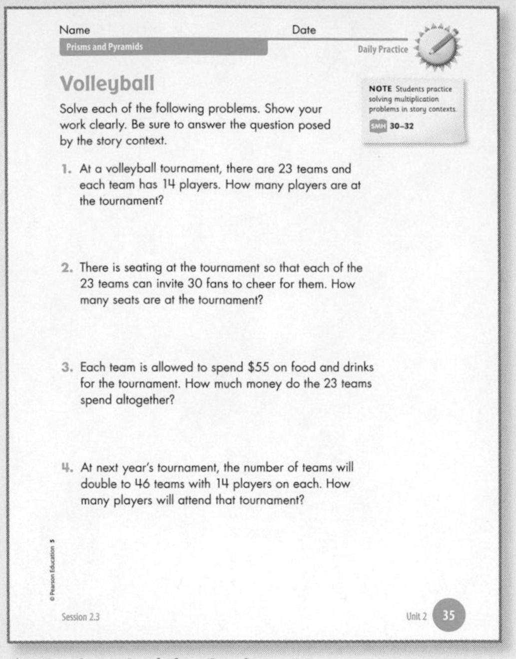
Name Date

Prisms and Pyramids — Daily Practice

Volleyball

Solve each of the following problems. Show your work clearly. Be sure to answer the question posed by the story context.

NOTE Students practice solving multiplication problems in story contexts.
SMH 30–32

1. At a volleyball tournament, there are 23 teams and each team has 14 players. How many players are at the tournament?

2. There is seating at the tournament so that each of the 23 teams can invite 30 fans to cheer for them. How many seats are at the tournament?

3. Each team is allowed to spend $55 on food and drinks for the tournament. How much money do the 23 teams spend altogether?

4. At next year's tournament, the number of teams will double to 46 teams with 14 players on each. How many players will attend that tournament?

© Pearson Education 5

Session 2.3 Unit 2 35

▲ Student Activity Book, p. 35

- When you multiplied the cubic meters along the length by the cubic meters along the width, what answer did you get? What does that number of cubic meters represent? *(the area of the floor and number of cubic meters that cover the floor and form the bottom layer)*
- What did you do next? Why? What does that number of cubic meters represent?

As students respond, listen for understanding that the number of cubes that cover the floor of the room represents the bottom layer and that the number of cubes that fit along the height represents the number of layers in the room. This reasoning demonstrates the ability to visualize what happens when we measure volume.

3 SESSION FOLLOW-UP
Daily Practice

Daily Practice: For ongoing review, have students complete *Student Activity Book* page 35.

Student Math Handbook: Students and families may use *Student Math Handbook* pages 105, 106–107 for reference and review. See pages 141–143 in the back of this unit.

Assessment: Measuring Volume in Cubic Centimeters

Math Focus Points

- Considering how the dimensions of a box change when the volume is changed (doubled, halved, or tripled)
- Determining the volume, in cubic centimeters, of a small prism

Today's Plan	Materials
1 MATH WORKSHOP **Measuring Volume** (60 MIN) 1A Boxes for Centimeter Cubes 1B Assessment: Measuring Volume in Cubic Centimeters	1A • *Student Activity Book*, pp. 36–37 • M18 1B • M24*; M25* ☑ • Centimeter cubes; centimeter rulers; calculators; scissors
2 SESSION FOLLOW-UP **Daily Practice**	• *Student Activity Book*, p. 38 • *Student Math Handbook*, pp. 106–107, 108

*See *Materials to Prepare,* p. 63.

Ten-Minute Math

Estimation and Number Sense Using Digit Cards, create two 3-digit by 2-digit division problems, (__ __ __ ÷ __ __). Give students 30 seconds to mentally estimate a quotient as close as possible to the exact answer. Students may jot down partial quotients or products if they wish. Some students may be able to determine the exact answer. Have two or three students explain their work, and record these strategies on the board or overhead.

MATH WORKSHOP

1 Measuring Volume

60 MIN

In this Math Workshop, students revisit an activity from Investigation 1, changing the dimensions of a box to double its volume and then dividing it in half. In this activity, the dimensions of the box are given in centimeters (3 cm x 4 cm x 6 cm), and students work in pairs. Students are also observed as they measure the volume of an unmarked box in cubic centimeters. For this assessment, you will need to observe each student individually. Therefore, consider having half of the students work on the assessment while the other half works on *Student Activity Book* pages 36–37.

1A Boxes for Centimeter Cubes

PAIRS

Using *Student Activity Book* pages 36–37, students use the dimensions (in centimeters) of a box to find two boxes to hold double the number and two boxes to hold half the number of centimeter cubes as the original box. They draw the patterns for the new boxes on centimeter grid paper.

ONGOING ASSESSMENT: Observing Students at Work

Students explore the relationship between the dimensions of a box and doubling or halving the number of centimeter cubes in the box.

- **Do students understand the relationship between changing the dimensions of a box and how many cubes will fit in the box?**
- **How do students solve this problem?** Do they double or halve the number of cubes and then figure out what the dimensions could be? Do they double or halve one or more of the dimensions to see how many cubes would be needed?

DIFFERENTIATION: Supporting the Range of Learners

Extension Ask students who need a challenge to find a box to hold *four* times the number of centimeter cubes as the 3 cm x 4 cm x 6 cm box.

Name Date

Prisms and Pyramids

Boxes for Centimeter Cubes (page 1 of 2)

You have a box that is 3 centimeters by 4 centimeters by 6 centimeters.

1. How many centimeter cubes does it hold? ________
   How do you know?

Find two boxes that will hold **twice** as many centimeter cubes as the box above.

2. **a.** What are the dimensions of each new box?
   Dimensions of first box: ________
   Dimensions of second box: ________
   b. Explain how you found the answers.

3. Draw the designs for the new boxes on centimeter grid paper.

© Pearson Education 5

36 Unit 2 Session 2.4

▲ Student Activity Book, p. 36

Name Date

Prisms and Pyramids

Boxes for Centimeter Cubes (page 2 of 2)

Find two boxes that will hold **half** as many centimeter cubes as the 3 centimeters by 4 centimeters by 6 centimeters box.

4. **a.** What are the dimensions of each new box?
   Dimensions of first box: ________
   Dimensions of second box: ________
   b. Explain how you found the answers.

5. Draw the designs for the new boxes on centimeter grid paper.

Challenge: Find a box that will hold **four** times as many centimeter cubes as the 3 centimeters by 4 centimeters by 6 centimeters box. Write the dimensions of the new box and explain how you found your answer.

© Pearson Education 5

Session 2.4 Unit 2 37

▲ Student Activity Book, p. 37

1B Assessment: Measuring Volume in Cubic Centimeters

INDIVIDUALS

In this observed assessment, students work individually to first cut out and tape together an unmarked, 6 cm x 8 cm x 3 cm box from Assessment: Measuring Volume in Cubic Centimeters (M24). They find the volume of the box and record their answer and the strategies they used to find the volume on a separate sheet of paper. This assessment addresses Benchmark 2 for this unit: *Use standard units to measure volume.* ❶

Assessment Checklist: Measuring Volume in Cubic Centimeters (M25) is provided to enable you to record your observations of how each student approaches this task. Each checklist has space to record observations for six students.

You are likely to observe different approaches to measuring the dimensions of the box. Some students will use centimeter rulers, and others may use centimeter cubes lined up along the edges of the box. Similarly, some students may use a layer approach, multiplying the cubes that form the bottom layer by the number of layers in the box, and others will simply multiply length x width x height. ❷

Students use various approaches to determine volume. As long as they measure the three dimensions accurately and are able to find the volume by using the dimensions, any approach is acceptable.

Teaching Notes

❶ **Photocopier Distortion** Be aware that some photocopiers may slightly distort the dimensions of the box on M24. Therefore, check the dimensions after you make copies and, if necessary, let students know that they should round their measurements to the nearest centimeter.

❷ **Computation and Measurement Errors** Some students may demonstrate understanding of the structure of rectangular prisms and how to determine their volume but may make computation or measurement errors as they do so. These students can often self-correct when asked to demonstrate their strategies.

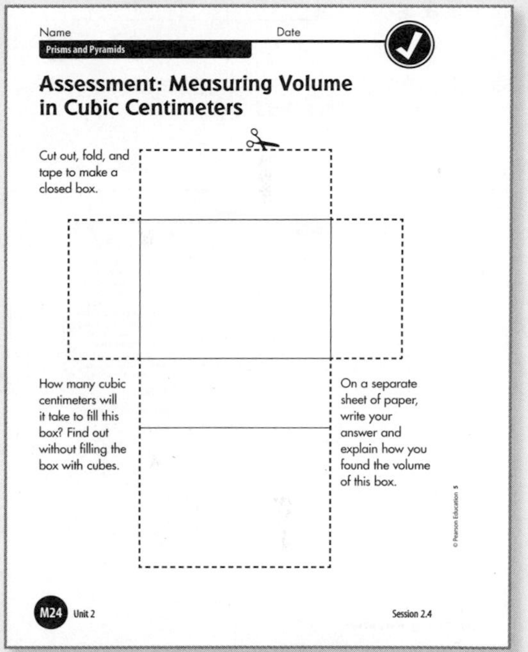

Name Date

Prisms and Pyramids

Assessment: Measuring Volume in Cubic Centimeters

Cut out, fold, and tape to make a closed box.

How many cubic centimeters will it take to fill this box? Find out without filling the box with cubes.

On a separate sheet of paper, write your answer and explain how you found the volume of this box.

© Pearson Education 5

M24 Unit 2 Session 2.4

▲ Resource Masters, M24

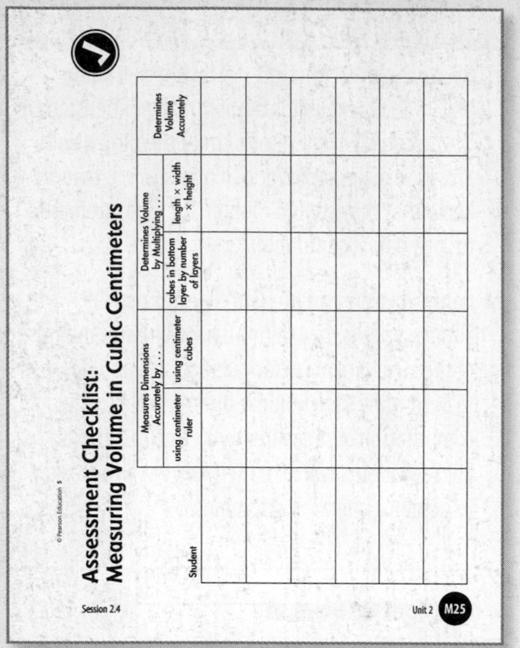

Assessment Checklist: Measuring Volume in Cubic Centimeters

Student	Measures Dimensions Accurately by . . . using centimeter ruler	using centimeter cubes	Determines Volume by Multiplying . . . cubes in bottom layer by number of layers	length × width × height	Determines Volume Accurately

Session 2.4 Unit 2 M25

▲ Resource Masters, M25

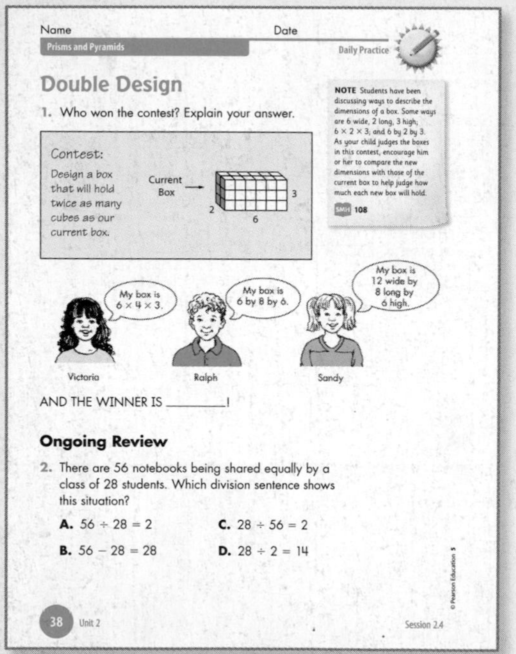

Name Date

Prisms and Pyramids Daily Practice

Double Design

1. Who won the contest? Explain your answer.

Contest: Design a box that will hold twice as many cubes as our current box.

Current Box 3 2 6

My box is 6 × 4 × 3.
My box is 6 by 8 by 6.
My box is 12 wide by 8 long by 6 high.
Victoria
Ralph
Sandy

NOTE Students have been discussing ways to describe the dimensions of a box. Some ways are 6 wide, 2 long, 3 high; 6 × 2 × 3; and 6 by 2 by 3. As your child judges the boxes in this contest, encourage him or her to compare the new dimensions with those of the current box to help judge how much each new box will hold.

SMH 108

AND THE WINNER IS ________!

Ongoing Review

2. There are 56 notebooks being shared equally by a class of 28 students. Which division sentence shows this situation?

A. 56 ÷ 28 = 2 **C.** 28 ÷ 56 = 2

B. 56 − 28 = 28 **D.** 28 ÷ 2 = 14

38 Unit 2 Session 2.4

▲ Student Activity Book, p. 38

ONGOING ASSESSMENT: Observing Students at Work

Students are assessed on their ability to determine volume by using a standard unit of measure.

- **Do students accurately measure the dimensions of the box with the centimeter ruler or by placing cubes outside the box along each edge?**
- **Are students able to use their measurements to determine how many cubic centimeters will fill the bottom layer of the box?** Can they use the measurements to determine how many layers there will be?
- **How do students compute the volume of the box?** Are their answers accurate?
- **Do they record the volume in cubic centimeters?**

2 SESSION FOLLOW-UP
Daily Practice

Daily Practice: For ongoing review of this unit's content, have students complete *Student Activity Book* page 38.

Student Math Handbook: Students and families may use *Student Math Handbook* pages 106–107, 108 for reference and review. See pages 141–143 in the back of this unit.

INVESTIGATION 3

Mathematical Emphasis

Volume Structuring prisms, pyramids, cylinders, and cones and determining their volume

Math Focus Points

- Comparing volumes of different-shaped containers
- Finding volume relationships between solids, particularly those with the same base and height
- Building a prism with three times the volume of a given pyramid
- Demonstrating the 3:1 relationship between rectangular prisms and pyramids with the same base and height
- Finding volume, in cubic centimeters, of prisms, pyramids, cylinders, and cones

This Investigation also focuses on

- Describing and defending measurement methods
- Building geometric solids

Volume Relationships Among Solids

	Student Activity Book	Student Math Handbook	Professional Development: Read Ahead of Time	
SESSION 3.1 p. 90				
Comparing Volumes Students compare volumes of common household containers. First they determine order, and then they employ direct comparison by using sand or rice. They make geometric solids for use in the rest of the investigation.	39–41	111–114	• **Teacher Note:** Student Methods for Comparing Containers, p. 125	
SESSION 3.2 p. 95				
Finding a Three-to-One Relationship Using rice or sand, students compare the volumes of related pairs of shapes (pyramids and prisms, cylinders and cones, with each pair having equal base and/or height measurements).	39, 43	111–114	• **Teacher Note:** Geometric Solids and Their Parts, p. 126 • **Dialogue Box:** Exploring the Three-to-One Relationship, p. 139	
SESSION 3.3 p. 99				
Prism and Pyramid Partners Given a rectangular pyramid, students design a rectangular prism with three times the volume of the pyramid. They also are given patterns for a pyramid and a cube to build a visual model of the 3:1 relationship.	44–45	111–114		
SESSION 3.4 p. 105				
Using Standard Units of Volume Students find the volume, in cubic centimeters, of the 11 solids (prisms, pyramids, cylinders, and cones) they have been using.	47–48	111–114		
SESSION 3.5 p. 110				
End-of-Unit Assessment Students solve two problems assessing their understanding of volume.	49–50	108, 111–114	• **Teacher Note:** End-of-Unit Assessment, p. 128	

Ten-Minute Math See page 16 for an overview.

Quick Images: 3-D

- T28–T29, *Quick Images: 3:D* (Images 15–20) [overhead transparency]
- Connecting cubes (20 per student)

Estimation and Number Sense

- M13–M15, Digit Cards

Materials to Gather	Materials to Prepare
• **Rice or sand** • **Sealable plastic bags** • **Paper bags** • **Containers** (from students) • **Scissors** (1 per student) • **Tape** (as needed)	• **M26–M30, Solid Patterns A–I** Make copies on cardstock, if possible. (1 set per pair) • **Numbered bags** Sort containers that students have brought in, putting 3 containers with different shapes, but similar volume, in paper bags. Number the bags. • **Rice (or sand) stations** Prepare rice or sand trays at several stations. Put a half-pound of rice or sand in sealable plastic bags. Also, have some sort of tray for catching spills. Another alternative is to put a larger amount of rice or sand in large plastic containers and have groups of 4 students share.
• **Solids** (made from M26–M30 in Session 3.1) • **Rice (or sand) stations** (from Session 3.1)	• **Chart** Create a chart on the board with 3 columns and 7 rows. The heading for column 1 is "Pair." Under this heading, write the numbers 1–6. Column 2 contains the heading "Solids." Underneath this heading, write the 2 related solids from M26–M30 next to each other. Next to pair "1," write solids: "A, B." Continue down the column (Pair 2: "C, D"; Pair 3: "E, F", and so on). Column 3 contains the heading "Number of Smaller Solids Needed to Fill Larger Solid." In this column, you will record class responses. See p. 96 for example.
• **Scissors** (1 per student) • **Tape** (as needed)	• **M31, Pyramid and Prism Partners** Make copies. (1 per student) • **M18, Centimeter Grid Paper** Make copies. (as needed) • **M32, Puzzle Cube Pattern** Make copies. (1 per student) • **M33, Puzzle Pyramid Pattern** Make copies. (1 per student)
• **Solids A–K** (made from M26–M30 in Session 3.1) • **Rice (or sand) stations** (from Session 3.1) • **Scissors** (as needed) • **Tape** (as needed) • **Centimeter cubes** (as needed) • **Rulers** (as needed)	• **T34, M34 See-Through Graduated Prism Patterns** [overhead transparency] Use M34 to make copies on transparency sheets. (1 per pair) • **Chart** On the board, create a chart with 2 columns and 13 rows. The first column is headed "Solid." The first row in that column reads "See-Through Prism." For the rest of the rows of the "Solid" column, write the letters A–K (referring to the solids created on M26–M30). The heading for the second column is "Volume (cubic centimeters)." In this column, you will record class responses. See p. 106 for example.
	• **M35–M36, End-of-Unit Assessment** Make copies. (1 each per student)

[overhead transparency icon] Overhead Transparency

Comparing Volumes

Math Focus Points

- Comparing volumes of different-shaped containers
- Building geometric solids

Today's Plan		Materials
1 ACTIVITY **Comparing Volumes of Containers**	20 MIN PAIRS	• Numbered paper bags with containers*; rice (sand) stations*
2 DISCUSSION **Comparing Volumes**	10 MIN CLASS	• Containers (from activity)
3 ACTIVITY **Making Solids from Patterns**	30 MIN PAIRS	• *Student Activity Book,* p. 39 • M26–M30* • Scissors; tape (as needed)
4 SESSION FOLLOW-UP **Daily Practice and Homework**		• *Student Activity Book,* pp. 40–41 • *Student Math Handbook,* pp. 111–114

*See *Materials to Prepare,* p. 89.

Ten-Minute Math

Quick Images: 3-D **Show Images 15–17 from *Quick Images: 3-D* (T28–T29) and follow the procedure for the basic routine. For each image, students discuss how they built their structures, including any revisions they made after each viewing. Ask students:**

- How did you remember the parts of the image?
- What did you notice about the relationship of the parts of the image?
- What helped you remember the whole image so that you could build your structure?

1 ACTIVITY
Comparing Volumes of Containers

20 MIN PAIRS

Place the rice or sand for measuring, the trays for catching spills, and the bags with containers in a central location. Point out that each bag has a number.

Over the past few days, you've been bringing in empty containers—jars and boxes and cans. I have put three of them in each of these bags. Each pair of you will take one bag to start with. First, place them in order just by looking at the containers. Your job is to rank the containers in the bag by their volumes, or the amount of space inside, from smallest to largest. Start by determining the order, and then measuring to check. Here's what to do:

- On a sheet of paper, write the number of the bag you have selected. Write or draw pictures to describe the order that you chose, and explain how you made the decision.
- Use rice (sand) with the containers to determine the actual order.
- Describe in writing the actual order and how you found it.

After you complete one bag of containers, try some other bags.

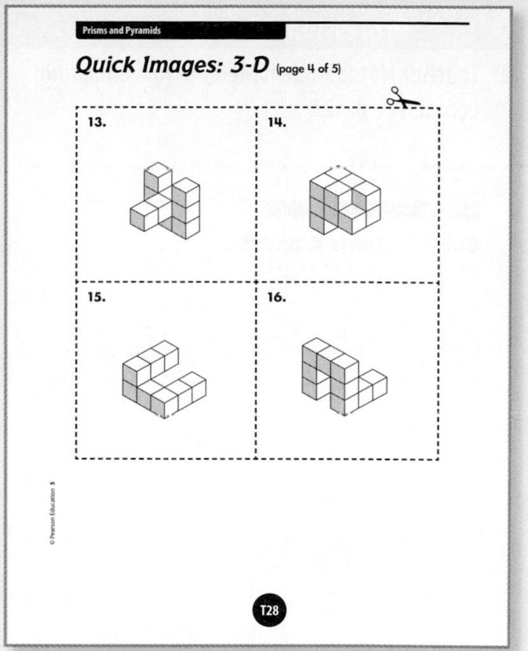

▲ Transparencies, T28

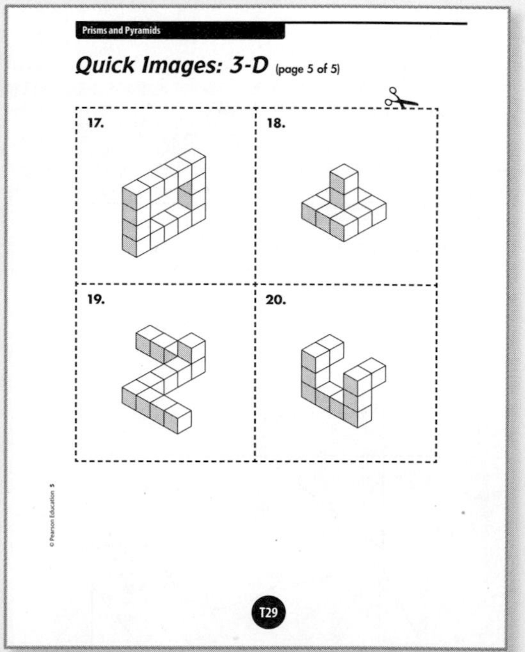

▲ Transparencies, T29

ONGOING ASSESSMENT: Observing Students at Work

Students compare volumes of containers, first by only looking at them and then by directly comparing them or using some other method.

- **Do students use compensation to place containers in order?** Do they say something like, "This shape is bigger at the bottom; but this other shape is taller, so I think they are the same"?
- **Do students compare each of the three containers separately, or can they draw logical conclusions about the relative sizes?** If they know that container X has a greater volume than container Y and that Y has a greater volume than Z, can they conclude that X has a greater volume than Z *without* directly comparing X and Z?
- **Do they use direct comparison for each container (pouring rice from one container to the other to determine which is smaller or larger) or do they use one container as a unit and count the number of times that this unit fills other containers?**
- **Are students paying attention to all three dimensions of the containers?** Do they think that a container that is taller has greater volume and not necessarily consider the size (area) of the base of the containers?

Professional Development

➊ **Teacher Note:** Student Methods for Comparing Containers, p. 125

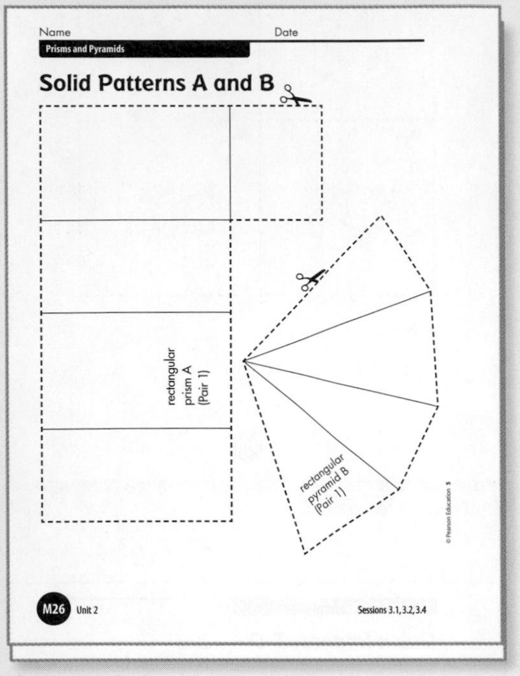
Name Date
Prisms and Pyramids
Solid Patterns A and B
rectangular prism A (Pair 1)
rectangular pyramid B (Pair 1)
© Pearson Education 5
M26 Unit 2 Sessions 3.1, 3.2, 3.4

▲ Resource Masters, M26–M27

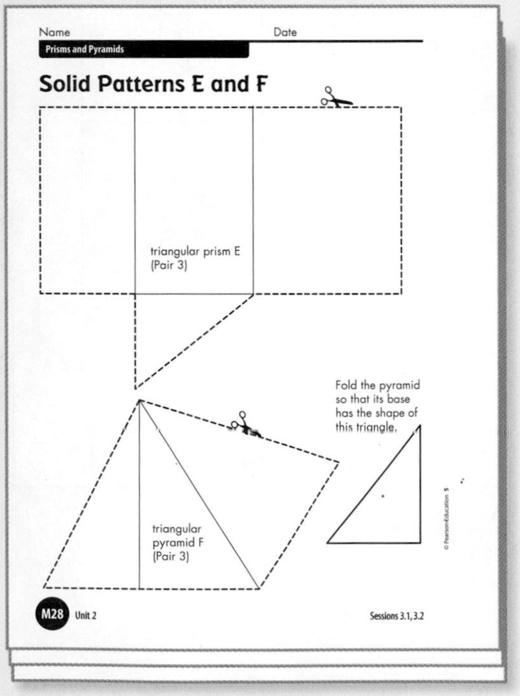
Name Date
Prisms and Pyramids
Solid Patterns E and F
triangular prism E (Pair 3)
Fold the pyramid so that its base has the shape of this triangle.
triangular pyramid F (Pair 3)
© Pearson Education 5
M28 Unit 2 Sessions 3.1, 3.2

▲ Resource Masters, M28–M30

DISCUSSION

2 Comparing Volumes

10 MIN CLASS

Math Focus Points for Discussion

- Comparing volumes of different-shaped containers

After about 20 minutes, hold a brief class discussion about which methods students used to order and measure volume.➊

What methods did you use to order the containers—both when you were just looking at them, and when you were measuring? Who used the same methods? Who used a different one?

Make sure that students show the containers they are talking about as they explain their strategies and their thinking. Otherwise it will be difficult for others to follow their descriptions.

Ask whether they got better at ordering the containers as they practiced, and what observations about the containers helped them decide.

- **Did you get better with deciding the order? Why?**
- **Did you notice anything about the containers that surprised you or helped you figure out something about volume?**
- **Talisha says that she started by comparing the heights but realizes now that the width of the container makes a difference. Do you have any thoughts about that?**

Students should notice that, as they consider the volume of a container, they have to pay attention to all of the dimensions, not just the height.

Students check their first answers by comparing the volume of each container with rice or sand.

ACTIVITY

3 Making Solids from Patterns

30 MIN PAIRS

Before starting Session 3.2, each pair of students should make 11 solids from Solid Patterns, A–K (M26–M30). Give each pair a copy of the Solid Patterns. Students also refer to *Student Activity Book* page 39, which shows what the patterns look like when cut out, folded, and taped together. Provide the pairs with some sort of container in which to store their solids.

Students cut and tape to create the prisms, pyramids, cylinders, and cones from the patterns. To get a sharp crease along the edges of the prisms and pyramids, it helps to draw first along the fold lines, pressing firmly with a ballpoint pen or pencil on the inside of the fold. Patterns should then be folded toward the scored line. Demonstrate how to make one of the cones or pyramids. Emphasize that when folding two sides together to be taped, these sides should meet exactly and not overlap. Have students apply tape along the entire length of the sides; otherwise it will be difficult to keep rice or sand inside the solids.❷

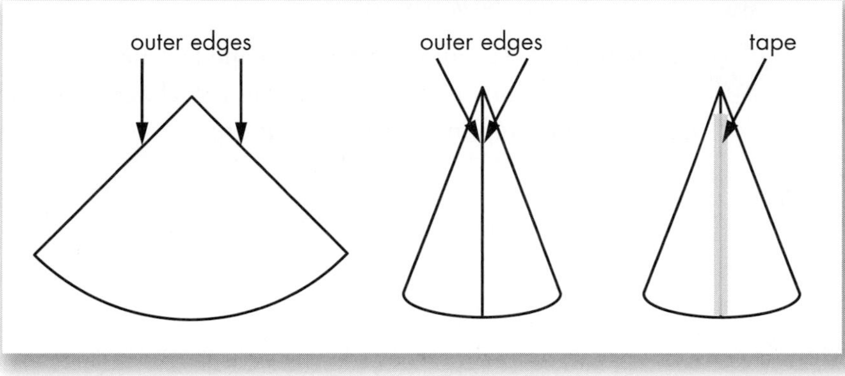

As students are working, check to make sure that they are making the solids correctly and taping the entire lengths of the sides. Encourage students to cut and tape as precisely as possible. Use this time to review with them the names of the geometric solids.

Teaching Note

❷ **Prism Patterns** The patterns for rectangular prisms (Solid Patterns A and I) are different from the box patterns used in Investigation 1, although they result in similar rectangular boxes. The patterns in Investigation 1 were designed to show the relationship between the sides of the pattern and the layers of the 3-D cube arrays. The pattern for this Investigation is more compact and designed to fit on the page with other patterns. If students seem confused by the new pattern, take a box from a pattern in Investigation 1 and demonstrate how it can be cut apart to make a pattern like Solid Patterns A and I.

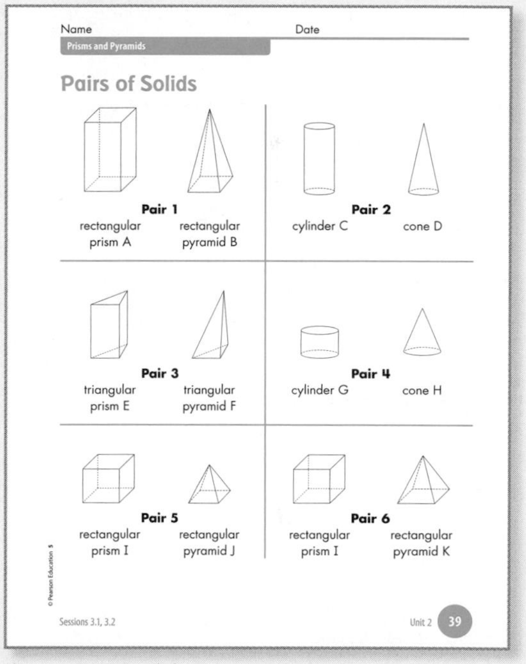
Name Date
Prisms and Pyramids
Pairs of Solids
Pair 1: rectangular prism A, rectangular pyramid B
Pair 2: cylinder C, cone D
Pair 3: triangular prism E, triangular pyramid F
Pair 4: cylinder G, cone H
Pair 5: rectangular prism I, rectangular pyramid J
Pair 6: rectangular prism I, rectangular pyramid K
© Pearson Education 5
Sessions 3.1, 3.2 Unit 2 39

▲ Student Activity Book, p. 39

Name Date

Prisms and Pyramids

Daily Practice

Coins

NOTE Students practice solving division problems in a money context.

SMH 38–39

Solve the following problems. Make sure that anyone looking at your work can tell how you solved the problem.

Alex, Nora, and Felix each won $27.75 in a contest.

1. Alex decided to collect his money all in quarters. How many quarters did he get?

2. Nora chose to get her prize all in dimes and nickels. Show 2 different possible combinations of dimes and nickels that would total $27.75.

   First way: Second way:

3. Felix wanted to collect his money in quarters, dimes, and nickels. Show 2 different possible combinations of quarters, dimes, and nickels that would total $27.75.

   First way: Second way:

© Pearson Education 5

40 Unit 2 Session 3.1

▲ Student Activity Book, p. 40

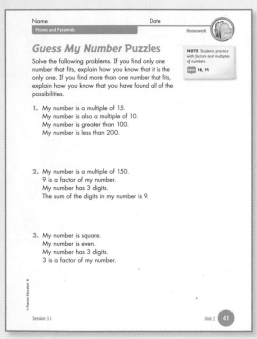

Name Date

Prisms and Pyramids

Homework

Guess My Number Puzzles

NOTE Students practice with factors and multiples of numbers.

SMH 18, 19

Solve the following problems. If you find only one number that fits, explain how you know that it is the only one. If you find more than one number that fits, explain how you know that you have found all of the possibilities.

1. My number is a multiple of 15.
   My number is also a multiple of 10.
   My number is greater than 100.
   My number is less than 200.

2. My number is a multiple of 150.
   9 is a factor of my number.
   My number has 3 digits.
   The sum of the digits in my number is 9.

3. My number is square.
   My number is even.
   My number has 3 digits.
   3 is a factor of my number.

© Pearson Education 5

Session 3.1 Unit 2 41

▲ Student Activity Book, p. 41

ONGOING ASSESSMENT: Observing Students at Work

Students build geometric solids from patterns.

- **Are students able to assemble the solids correctly?**
- **How do students determine how the components of the solids fold together to make the solid?** Are they able to visualize how the pattern fits together? Do they need to look constantly at the pictures on Student Activity Book page 39?

SESSION FOLLOW-UP

4 Daily Practice and Homework

Daily Practice: For ongoing review, have students complete *Student Activity Book* page 40.

Homework: Students use clues to solve number puzzles on *Student Activity Book* page 41.

Student Math Handbook: Students and families may use *Student Math Handbook* pages 111–114 for reference and review. See pages 141–143 in the back of this unit.

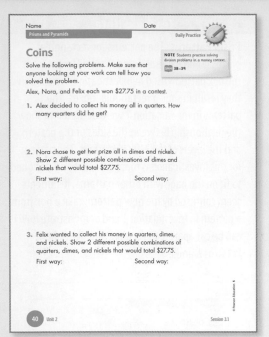

Finding a Three-to-One Relationship

Math Focus Points

- Finding volume relationships between solids, particularly those with the same base and height

Vocabulary

pyramid
cylinder
cone

Today's Plan			Materials
ACTIVITY 1 **Comparing Solids and Their Volumes**	45 MIN	PAIRS	• *Student Activity Book,* p. 39 (from Session 3.1) • Student-made solids (from Session 3.1); rice (or sand) stations; chart*
DISCUSSION 2 **Related Solids**	15 MIN	CLASS	
SESSION FOLLOW-UP 3 **Daily Practice**			• *Student Activity Book,* p. 43 • *Student Math Handbook,* pp. 111–114

*See *Materials to Prepare,* p. 89.

Ten-Minute Math

Quick Images: 3-D **Show Images 18–20 from *Quick Images: 3-D* (T29) and follow the procedure for the basic routine. For each image, students discuss how they built their structures, including any revisions they made after each viewing. Ask students:**

- How did you remember the parts of the image?
- What did you notice about the relationship of the parts of the image?
- What helped you remember the whole image so that you could build your structure?

Teaching Note

❶ **Set of Solids** Student pairs should have made all 11 solids before starting this session. If they have not, allow time for them to finish before starting this activity.

Professional Development

❷ **Teacher Note:** Geometric Solids and Their Parts, p. 126

Math Notes

❸ **Measurement Imprecisions** Because there are likely to be some measurement and construction errors in these activities, students will not all get exactly the same answers. Suggest that they round their answers to their nearest whole or half unit. If necessary, have a brief discussion to recognize when answers are "close enough."

❹ **A Three-to-One Relationship** If their cutting and taping is fairly accurate, students should discover that the volume of each larger, flat-topped solid is about three times the volume of the smaller, pointed solid, *if it has the same base and height.* (Because of inevitable measurement and construction errors, the three-to-one relationship will not be exact.)

ACTIVITY 1

45 MIN PAIRS

Comparing Solids and Their Volumes

Before introducing the activity, spend a few minutes having students name the different types of solids—rectangular and triangular prisms, pyramids, cylinders, and cones.❶ Students have worked with these solids in Grades 3 and 4. Being able to identify the solids with correct terminology is useful for class discussions in this Investigation. As students work with these solids, help them remember what the characteristics of prisms, pyramids, cylinders, and cones are (bases, faces, vertices, edges, and so on).❷

Call attention to the way the solids are grouped on *Student Activity Book* page 39.

Look carefully at the two solids in each pair. Think about how they are the same and how they are different. Take the solids you have made from the patterns and pair them the same way. Use your rice [or sand] to find how the volume of the larger solid compares with that of the smaller solid in each pair. We're going to record your findings on this chart I have on the board. Work in pairs to complete this task.

Pair	Solids	Number of Smaller Solid Needed to Fill Larger Solid
1	A, B	
2	C, D	
3	E, F	
4	G, H	
5	I, J	
6	I, K	

Students use whatever methods they choose to compare the volumes of the solids. To contain the rice or sand as much as possible, ask students to do their pouring over the trays.❸ ❹

Make the chart wide enough for all students to record their answers. Most find a three-to-one relationship for appropriate pairs of solids. Seeing such numbers recorded on the class chart encourages those students who find a different relationship to reflect on possible errors.

ONGOING ASSESSMENT: Observing Students at Work

Students compare volume of solids.

- **How accurately do students measure?** Do they overfill (or underfill) the solids?
- **Do students notice the relationships between the bases and heights of the pairs of solids?**

As you circulate, encourage students to think about how the solids in each pair compare. Ask questions such as these:

What do you notice about the bases of the solids that are paired? What about the height? Each pair of solids in pairs 1–3 have the same base and height; the solids in pair 4 have the same base but different heights. In pairs 5 and 6, rectangular pyramids J and K have the same height as rectangular prism I, but only pyramid K has the same base as rectangular prism I.

2 DISCUSSION

Related Solids

15 MIN CLASS

Math Focus Points for Discussion

- Finding volume relationships between solids, particularly those with the same base and height

After everyone has compared the volumes of the solids in all six pairs and recorded their data on the class chart, bring the students together to discuss their findings.

- What did you discover? How do the volumes of the solids in each pair compare?
- How are the shapes of the solids in each pair the same, and how are they different?

The goal of this discussion is for students to recognize that if a prism or a cylinder has the same height and base as a pyramid or cone, then the volume of the prism or cylinder is three times that of the pyramid or cone. This relationship may be difficult for students to explain fully.

Professional Development

5 **Dialogue Box:** Exploring the Three-to-One Relationship, p. 139

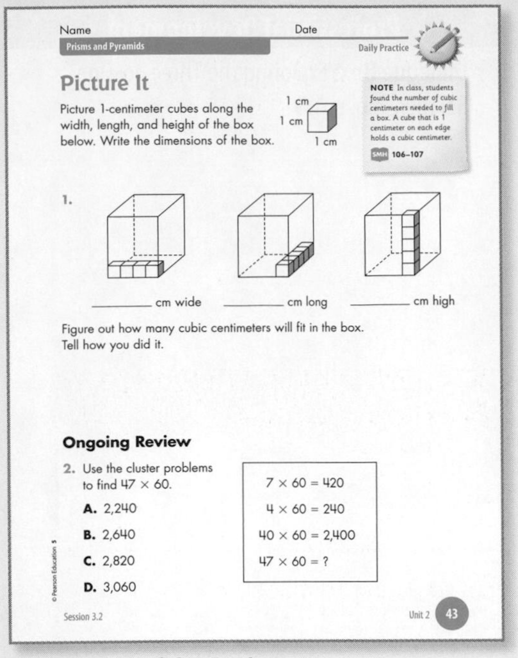
Name Date
Prisms and Pyramids
Daily Practice

Picture It

Picture 1-centimeter cubes along the width, length, and height of the box below. Write the dimensions of the box.

1 cm, 1 cm, 1 cm

NOTE In class, students found the number of cubic centimeters needed to fill a box. A cube that is 1 centimeter on each edge holds a cubic centimeter.

SMH 106–107

1.

_______ cm wide _______ cm long _______ cm high

Figure out how many cubic centimeters will fit in the box. Tell how you did it.

Ongoing Review

2. Use the cluster problems to find 47 × 60.

A. 2,240

B. 2,640

C. 2,820

D. 3,060

7 × 60 = 420
4 × 60 = 240
40 × 60 = 2,400
47 × 60 = ?

© Pearson Education 5

Session 3.2 Unit 2 43

▲ Student Activity Book, p. 43

To communicate their findings clearly, students need to agree on the meanings for the terms *base* and *height* and about methods for measuring the height of cones and pyramids.

Students compare volume between solids.

As you wrap up the discussion, ask students to save their solids to use again in Session 3.4.

SESSION FOLLOW-UP
3 Daily Practice

Daily Practice: For ongoing review of this unit's content, have students complete *Student Activity Book* page 43.

Student Math Handbook: Students and families may use *Student Math Handbook* pages 111–114 for reference and review. See pages 141–143 in the back of this unit.

Prism and Pyramid Partners

Math Focus Points

- Building a prism with three times the volume of a given pyramid
- Demonstrating the 3:1 relationship between rectangular prisms and pyramids with the same base and height

Today's Plan		Materials
ACTIVITY **1 Designing a Prism**	25 MIN INDIVIDUALS	• M31*; M18* • Scissors; tape
DISCUSSION **2 Prisms We Made**	15 MIN CLASS	• Prisms and pyramids made from M31 (from Activity 1)
ACTIVITY **3 Puzzle Patterns**	20 MIN INDIVIDUALS	• M32*; M33* • Scissors; tape
SESSION FOLLOW-UP **4 Daily Practice and Homework**		• *Student Activity Book,* pp. 44–45 • *Student Math Handbook,* pp. 111–114

*See *Materials to Prepare,* p. 89.

Ten-Minute Math

Estimation and Number Sense Using Digit Cards, create two 3-digit by 2-digit division problems, (__ __ __ ÷ __ __). Give students 30 seconds to mentally estimate a quotient as close as possible to the exact answer. Students may jot down partial quotients or products if they wish. Some students may be able to determine the exact answer. Have two or three students explain their work, and record these strategies on the board or overhead.

Teaching Note

➊ **Different Prisms Are Possible** When students have finished, ask them to bring their prisms and written explanations for a class discussion. Students have probably discovered a variety of prisms that have three times the volume of the pyramid.

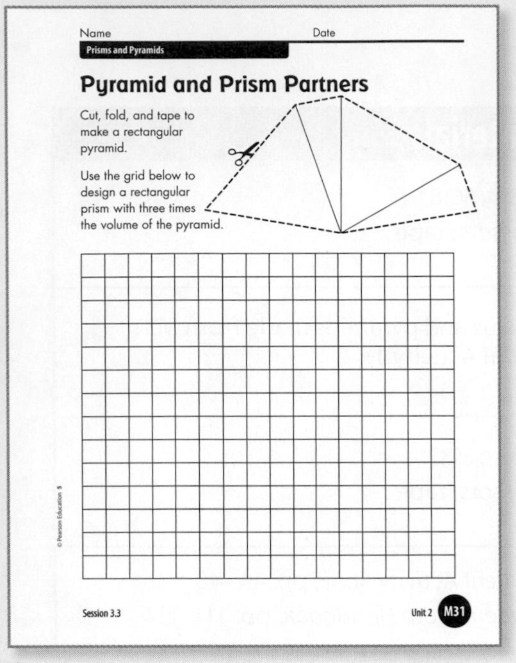
Name Date

Prisms and Pyramids

Pyramid and Prism Partners

Cut, fold, and tape to make a rectangular pyramid.

Use the grid below to design a rectangular prism with three times the volume of the pyramid.

© Pearson Education 5

Session 3.3 Unit 2 M31

▲ Resource Masters, M31

ACTIVITY

25 MIN INDIVIDUALS

1 Designing a Prism

In the six solid pairs that you worked with earlier, some of the solids had three times the volume of their partner solid. Pyramid and Prism Partners (M31) gives you a pattern for another rectangular pyramid. You'll cut out and make the pyramid. Then you'll make a "partner" for this pyramid, a rectangular prism that has three times the volume of the pyramid. When you're done building your rectangular prism, write an explanation about how you decided what size to make it.

Students make the pattern for the prism from the grid at the bottom of the sheet. They check their solutions with rice (or sand) or any other method they choose. Have copies of Centimeter Grid Paper (M18) for students who need extra copies.

Some students who have discovered the three-to-one relationship between prisms and pyramids that have the same base and height may not yet understand under what conditions this relationship holds. Encourage students to consider the attributes of each solid and then write their explanations.

Some students may recognize that if they make a prism with the same base and height as the pyramid (2 cm x 6 cm x 5 cm), it has three times the volume. They can determine the approximate height (5 cm) by setting the pyramid next to a ruler held vertically. If they use the length of an edge for the height (6 cm), their prism has *more* than three times the volume. Do not tell students this; have them discover it on their own because it helps them understand and remember how to think about the height of nonprism solids.

Other students devise methods to make a prism with a different base that still has triple the volume of the pyramid. For example, they may start with a prism whose faces are too high, fill it with three times the volume of the pyramid, and then cut off the extra length on the sides. This is a valid method.➊

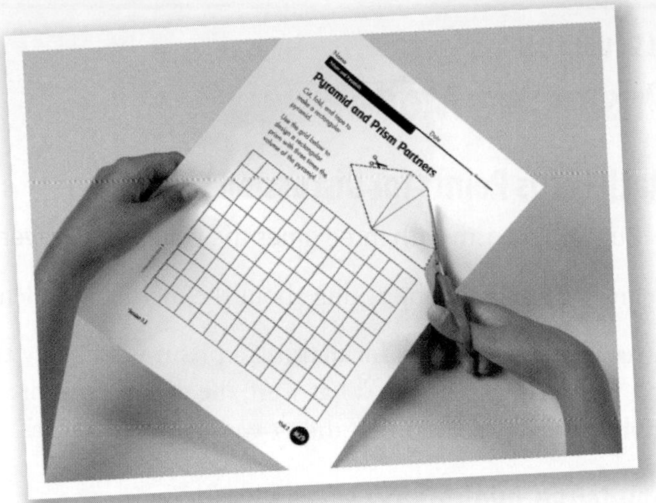

Students experiment with different strategies to find solids that fit the three-to-one relationship.

ONGOING ASSESSMENT: Observing Students at Work

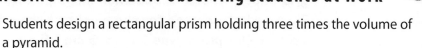

Students design a rectangular prism holding three times the volume of a pyramid.

- **What strategies do students use to find the prism?** Do they build a prism with the same base and height as the pyramid?
- **How do they determine the height of the pyramid?**
- **Do they make a prism, fill it three times with rice from the pyramid, and then cut off the sides?**
- **Do they use trial and error, making different prisms, and adjusting the size when it does not hold three times the volume until they find a prism that works?**

Although the last method does not make use of the three-to-one relationship, it is a valid method.

DIFFERENTIATION: Supporting the Range of Learners

Intervention After allowing an appropriate amount of time for discovery, help students who are unable to get started on this task by asking questions such as these:

Does the work we did yesterday with pairs A and B and I and K give you any idea about how to start? What did you notice about how the pyramids and prisms in each of these pairs are similar? What does that tell you about the prism you need to build in this activity?

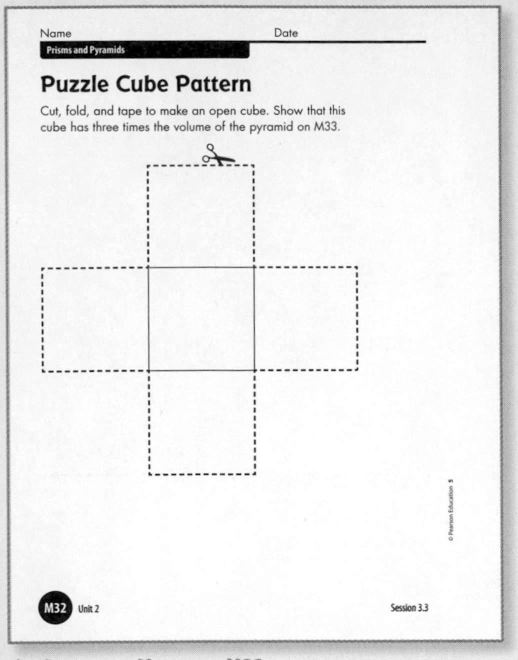
Name Date

Prisms and Pyramids

Puzzle Cube Pattern

Cut, fold, and tape to make an open cube. Show that this cube has three times the volume of the pyramid on M33.

© Pearson Education 5

M32 Unit 2 Session 3.3

▲ Resource Masters, M32

DISCUSSION

2 Prisms We Made

15 MIN CLASS

Math Focus Points for Discussion

- Building a prism with three times the volume of a given pyramid

Begin the discussion by asking about the methods students used.

What methods worked for making a prism with three times the volume of the pyramid? What were the dimensions of your prism? Did anybody try a method that didn't work? What was it?

Students might say:

"Janet and I remembered that if the base and height are the same, a prism has three times the volume. So we put the base of the pyramid on the grid paper, traced it, and then measured its height. That's what we used for the height of the prism. It worked. Our prism was 2 cm x 6 cm x 5 cm."

"Georgia and I kind of did it the same. We put the pyramid on the grid paper and traced the base. Then we just made a tall prism. We filled the pyramid with rice three times and poured it into the prism. Then we just cut off the prism at the level of the rice. Our prism had the same dimensions—2 cm x 6 cm x 5 cm."

"I wish Avery and I had thought of putting the base of the pyramid on the grid paper! We did a similar thing as Alicia and Georgia, though. We made a prism that had a base of 4 cm x 5 cm and made it tall. We poured the rice from the pyramid three times and then cut the prism at the top of the rice. Our dimensions were 4 cm x 5 cm x 3 cm."

After students discuss their methods and prove that the prism has three times the volume of the pyramid, ask them to compare the different prisms they made.

Do the different prisms we built have the same volume or different volumes?

It may not be clear to everyone that all of the prisms with three times the volume of the pyramid have equal volume, even if they look different. If needed, test the different prisms with students by directly comparing their volumes with rice or sand.

3 ACTIVITY

Puzzle Patterns

20 MIN INDIVIDUALS

Students use Puzzle Cube Pattern (M32) and Puzzle Pyramid Pattern (M33) to build a visual model of the three-to-one relationship between prisms and pyramids with the same height. ❷

Make the solids from these pages, one open cube and three pyramids. Then, figure out how to put the pyramids together so that they make a cube that fits into the cube box.

As students are working, ask them how the pyramids and the prism are the same (they have the same base and height).

ONGOING ASSESSMENT: Observing Students at Work

Students build three pyramids that fit into a cube.

- **Are students able to fit the three pyramids inside the cube?**
- **Do students recognize that the volume of the prism is three times the volume of the pyramid or that the volume of the pyramid is one third that of the prism?**

Students investigate the three-to-one relationship of prisms and pyramids that have the same base and height.

Math Note

❷ **Pyramids and a Prism** This puzzle offers a visual demonstration of the three-to-one volume relationship between prisms and pyramids with the same height and base. However, although a rectangular prism can always be decomposed into three pyramids with the same volume, in general, these three pyramids will not be identical. Because a cube has equal lengths for each dimension, the three pyramids are identical, so the cube is a special case.

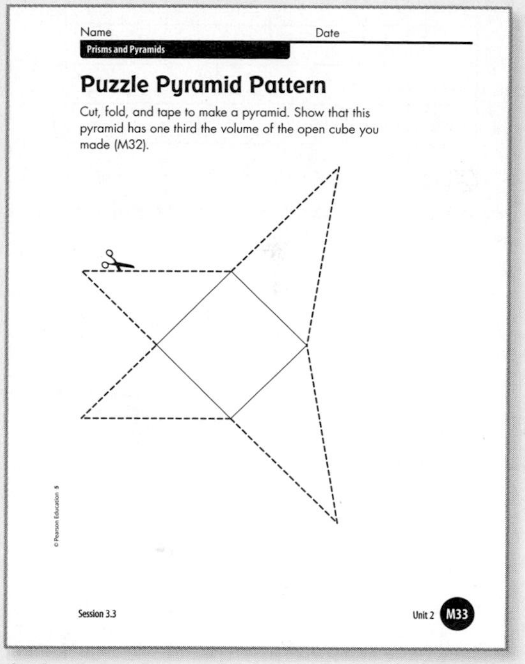

Name Date

Prisms and Pyramids

Puzzle Pyramid Pattern

Cut, fold, and tape to make a pyramid. Show that this pyramid has one third the volume of the open cube you made (M32).

© Pearson Education 5

Session 3.3 Unit 2 M33

▲ Resource Masters, M33

Name Date

Prisms and Pyramids

Daily Practice

Division Practice

Solve each division problem below. Then write the related multiplication combination.

NOTE Students review division problems that are related to known multiplication combinations.

SMH 14, 25–29

Division Problem	Multiplication Combination
1. 54 ÷ 9 = ______	______ × ______ = ______
2. 55 ÷ 5 = ______	______ × ______ = ______
3. 56 ÷ 8 = ______	______ × ______ = ______
4. 84 ÷ 12 = ______	______ × ______ = ______
5. 63 ÷ 9 = ______	______ × ______ = ______
6. 96 ÷ 8 = ______	______ × ______ = ______
7. 72 ÷ 9 = ______	______ × ______ = ______
8. 64 ÷ 8 = ______	______ × ______ = ______
9. 81 ÷ 9 = ______	______ × ______ = ______
10. 108 ÷ 12 = ______	______ × ______ = ______

© Pearson Education 5

44 Unit 2 Session 3.3

▲ **Student Activity Book, p. 44**

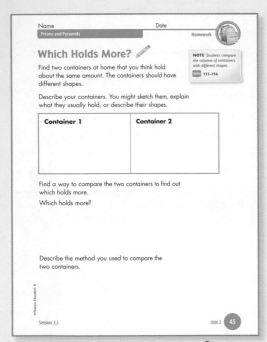

Name Date

Prisms and Pyramids

Homework

Which Holds More?

Find two containers at home that you think hold about the same amount. The containers should have different shapes.

NOTE Students compare the volumes of containers with different shapes.

SMH 111–114

Describe your containers. You might sketch them, explain what they usually hold, or describe their shapes.

Container 1	Container 2

Find a way to compare the two containers to find out which holds more.

Which holds more?

Describe the method you used to compare the two containers.

© Pearson Education 5

Session 3.3 Unit 2 45

▲ **Student Activity Book, p. 45** WRITING

DIFFERENTIATION: Supporting the Range of Learners

Extension Ask students who need a challenge to think about a way to determine the actual volume (in cubic centimeters) of the cube and pyramid. If they are not sure how to do this, remind them of the activity in Session 2.1. (Finding actual volume of the solid pairs happens in Session 3.4.)

4 SESSION FOLLOW-UP

Daily Practice and Homework

Daily Practice: For ongoing review, have students complete *Student Activity Book* page 44.

Homework: On *Student Activity Book* page 45, students find two containers with different shapes that they believe hold about the same amount, and then they compare the volume of the containers.

Student Math Handbook: Students and families may use *Student Math Handbook* pages 111–114 for reference and review. See pages 141–143 in the back of this unit.

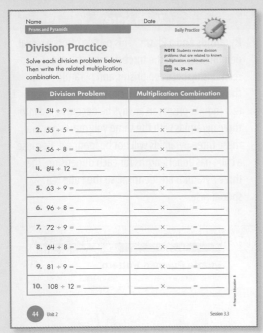

Using Standard Units of Volume

Math Focus Points

- Finding volume, in cubic centimeters, of prisms, pyramids, cylinders, and cones

Today's Plan		Materials
ACTIVITY **1 Measuring with Cubic Centimeters**	50 MIN PAIRS	• T34* • See-through graduated prism*; student-made solids A–K (from Session 3.1); rice (sand) stations (from Session 3.1; as needed); scissors (as needed); tape (as needed); centimeter cubes (as needed); rulers (as needed); chart paper*
DISCUSSION **2 How We Found the Volume**	10 MIN CLASS	• Chart: "Volume of Solids"*
SESSION FOLLOW-UP **3 Daily Practice and Homework**		• *Student Activity Book*, pp. 47–48 • *Student Math Handbook*, pp. 111–114

*See *Materials to Prepare*, p. 89.

Ten-Minute Math

Estimation and Number Sense Using Digit Cards, create two 3-digit by 2-digit division problems, (_ _ _ ÷ _ _). Give students 30 seconds to mentally estimate a quotient as close as possible to the exact answer. Students may jot down partial quotients or products if they wish. Some students may be able to determine the exact answer. Have two or three students explain their work, and record these strategies on the board or overhead.

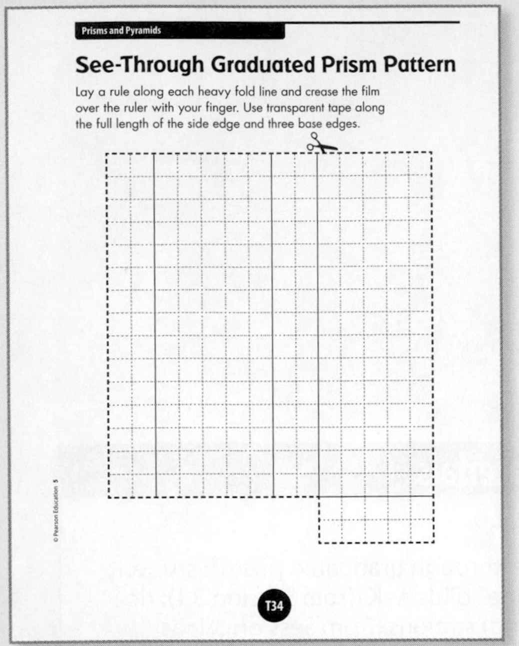
Prisms and Pyramids

See-Through Graduated Prism Pattern

Lay a rule along each heavy fold line and crease the film over the ruler with your finger. Use transparent tape along the full length of the side edge and three base edges.

T34

▲ transparencies, T34

ACTIVITY

50 MIN PAIRS

1 Measuring with Cubic Centimeters

Introduce the see-through prism that you made with See-Through Graduated Prism Pattern (T34), without telling students that it is a measuring device. (Because there are no numbers on the sides, only centimeter squares, it is not obviously a measuring tool.) Explain that in this activity, students find the volume of this prism as well as the volumes of Solids A–K they made in Session 3.1. If possible, make copies for student use on sturdy overhead transparencies (1 per pair).

In the last sessions, you compared the volumes of your different solids. Now your task is to find the actual volumes as measured in cubic centimeters.

You'll start with this see-through prism. How many centimeter cubes will it take to completely fill this prism? After you figure that out, you'll find the volume of Solid A, the rectangular prism.

Then you'll try Solid B, the rectangular pyramid [hold one up]. Of course, we can't really fill this pyramid with the centimeter cubes because we can't get cubes to fit into the pointed top. But volume is always measured in some sort of cubic unit; in this case we're using cubic centimeters. What if these centimeter cubes were made out of clay? Then we could squish them to fit into the pointed top or any other small space. Do you think you could find out how many "clay" cubic centimeters it would take to fill the rectangular pyramid?

Students find the volume of all 11 solids they made, measured in cubic centimeters. They can use rice (sand), centimeter cubes, rulers, or whatever other materials they want to use. While working in pairs, each student should keep his or her own records.

Make a chart on the board for students to record the volume they determine for each solid.

Solid	Volume (cubic centimeters)	Solid	Volume (cubic centimeters)
See-Through Prism		F	
A		G	
B		H	
C		I	
D		J	
E		K	

To find the number of cubic centimeters in the see-through prism and rectangular prism A, most students use the methods they developed in Investigation 1, using the dimensions of the figures. Some may still need to place actual centimeter cubes in the prisms, at least enough for the bottom layer.

Students use a variety of methods to determine the volume of the other solids. For example, they might approach rectangular pyramid B in one of the following ways:

- They might first find the volume of the rectangular prism A by multiplying its length, width, and height. Recalling that the volume of rectangular pyramid B is one-third of that, they divide their answer for the prism by 3 to get the volume of the pyramid. (Although this method clearly makes sense to adults, many students are still building their conceptual understanding of volume and dividing by 3 is not obvious.)
- They might fill the pyramid with rice, pour that rice into the see-through prism, and then determine how many cubic centimeters the rice has filled.

One student method might be to fill the pyramid with rice, pour it into the see-through prism, and measure the cubic centimeters.

Some students may propose to make a cubic centimeter box out of grid paper and use it to fill their solids with rice, one cubic centimeter at a time. This method works and shows understanding of the principles involved; however, it is impractical because of the larger number of cubic centimeters that fit in the solids. Encourage these students to find a more efficient method.❶

Teaching Note

❶ **Accuracy of See-Through Prisms** The prisms made from transparency film are not rigid and give less accurate measurements. The sides of the handmade prism bulge slightly as the rice is added, distorting the measurement. Students can minimize this distortion by pushing in the sides of the prism with their fingers, to keep the sides flat, especially near the top of the prism.

Some students may not think of using the see-through prism as a measuring device. You might suggest the idea with this question:

Can you think of a way this prism could help you find how many cubic centimeters fit in Solid B?

If that does not help, be more direct, modeling its use.

Let's fill Pyramid B with rice, and pour the rice into the see-through prism. How many cubic centimeters will it take to fill the see-through prism to the same level as the rice? Knowing that, how many cubic centimeters does it take to fill Pyramid B?

As students find the volumes of different solids, have them write their measurements on the class chart.

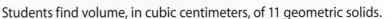

ONGOING ASSESSMENT: Observing Students at Work

Students find volume, in cubic centimeters, of 11 geometric solids.

- **What strategies are students using to find the volume (e.g., using only numbers, using the solids and rice and directly measuring, or other methods)?**
- **How accurate are students' measurements?**
- **As students record their answers on the class chart, do they notice discrepancies in their measurements?** Do they remeasure?

2 DISCUSSION

10 MIN CLASS

How We Found the Volume

Math Focus Points for Discussion

- Finding volume, in cubic centimeters, of prisms, pyramids, cylinders, and cones

After most of the pairs have measured the volume of the see-through prism and all 11 solids, proceed to the following questions:

- **What methods did you use for finding the volume of these solids?**
- **Why do you think these methods work?**
- **Did anybody try any methods that didn't work?**

Direct attention to the class chart on which student pairs have recorded the volume for each solid.

Let's look at the answers for each solid. Should we all get the same answers? Why didn't we?

For rectangular prisms, the volume measured with rice rarely matches exactly the volume found by multiplying the length, width, and height. Loosely taped or bulging sides can cause surprisingly large discrepancies. Therefore, it is important to evaluate students' methods, rather than their answers, to assess their understanding of the concepts and to make sure that students are clear why these inaccuracies exist.

If there are some answers that are very different from the rest, ask what methods were used to find these answers. What computations or measurements were performed? What were the answers to the computations?

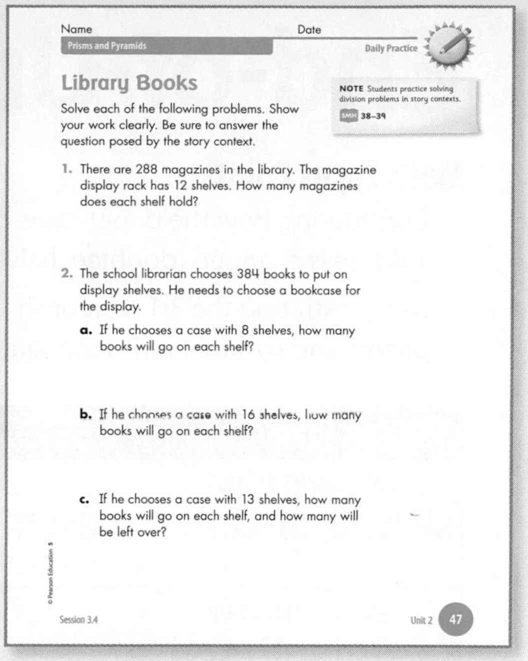
Name Date
Prisms and Pyramids
Daily Practice

Library Books

NOTE Students practice solving division problems in story contexts.
SMH 38–39

Solve each of the following problems. Show your work clearly. Be sure to answer the question posed by the story context.

1. There are 288 magazines in the library. The magazine display rack has 12 shelves. How many magazines does each shelf hold?

2. The school librarian chooses 384 books to put on display shelves. He needs to choose a bookcase for the display.
   a. If he chooses a case with 8 shelves, how many books will go on each shelf?
   b. If he chooses a case with 16 shelves, how many books will go on each shelf?
   c. If he chooses a case with 13 shelves, how many books will go on each shelf, and how many will be left over?

© Pearson Education 5
Session 3.4 Unit 2 47

▲ Student Activity Book, p. 47

3 SESSION FOLLOW-UP
Daily Practice and Homework

- **Daily Practice:** For ongoing review, have students complete *Student Activity Book* page 47.
- **Homework:** Given 2 different ways to start, students solve multiplication problems on *Student Activity Book* page 48.
- **Student Math Handbook:** Students and families may use *Student Math Handbook* pages 111–114 for reference and review. See pages 141–143 in the back of this unit.

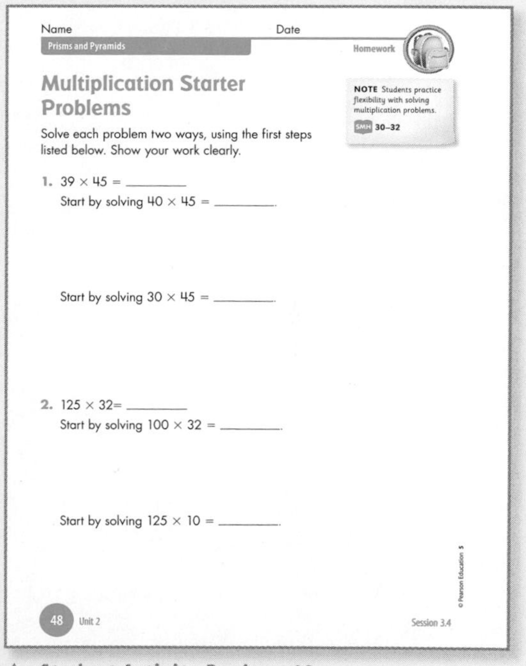
Name Date
Prisms and Pyramids
Homework

Multiplication Starter Problems

NOTE Students practice flexibility with solving multiplication problems.
SMH 30–32

Solve each problem two ways, using the first steps listed below. Show your work clearly.

1. $39 \times 45 =$ ______
   Start by solving $40 \times 45 =$ ______.
   Start by solving $30 \times 45 =$ ______.

2. $125 \times 32 =$ ______
   Start by solving $100 \times 32 =$ ______.
   Start by solving $125 \times 10 =$ ______.

© Pearson Education 5
48 Unit 2 Session 3.4

▲ Student Activity Book, p. 48

End-of-Unit Assessment

Math Focus Points

- Considering how the dimensions of a box change when the volume is changed (doubled, halved, or tripled)
- Demonstrating the 3:1 relationship between rectangular prisms and pyramids with the same base and height

Today's Plan	Materials
1 ASSESSMENT ACTIVITY **End-of-Unit Assessment** — 60 MIN, INDIVIDUALS	• M35–M36*
2 SESSION FOLLOW-UP **Daily Practice**	• *Student Activity Book*, pp. 49–50 • *Student Math Handbook*, pp. 108, 111–114

*See *Materials to Prepare*, p. 89.

Ten-Minute Math

Estimation and Number Sense Using Digit Cards, create two 3-digit by 2-digit division problems, (___ ___ ___ ÷ ___ ___). Give students 30 seconds to mentally estimate a quotient as close as possible to the exact answer. Students may jot down partial quotients or products if they wish. Some students may be able to determine the exact answer. Have two or three students explain their work, and record these strategies on the board or overhead.

1 ASSESSMENT ACTIVITY

End-of-Unit Assessment

60 MIN INDIVIDUALS

This End-of-Unit Assessment (M35–M36) consists of two problems. In the first problem, students are given the dimensions of a box and asked to find the dimensions of two new boxes containing three times the volume of the original box. This assessment addresses Benchmark 3: Identify how the dimensions of a box change when the volume is changed.

In the second question, students are asked to explain how to find the volume of a square pyramid. This assessment addresses Benchmark 4: Explain the relationship between the volumes of prisms and pyramids with the same base and height.①

ONGOING ASSESSMENT: Observing Students at Work

- **Do students understand how changing the dimensions of a box changes the volume (e.g., tripling one dimension triples the volume)?**
- **How do students solve this problem?** Do they triple the number of cubes (in this case from 54 to 162) and then figure out what the dimensions could be? Do they triple one or more of the dimensions to see how many cubes would be needed?
- **How do students explain finding the volume of the pyramid?** Do they explain that the volume of the pyramid would be one third of the volume of a prism with the same base and height? Do they discuss building the pyramid and filling it with rice or sand, and then measuring the volume of the rice or sand?

2 SESSION FOLLOW-UP

Daily Practice

Daily Practice: For reinforcement and enrichment of this unit's content, have students complete *Student Activity Book* pages 49–50.

Student Math Handbook: Students and families may use *Student Math Handbook* pages 108, 111–114 for reference and review. See pages 141–143 in the back of this unit.

Professional Development

① **Teacher Note:** End-of-Unit Assessment, p. 128

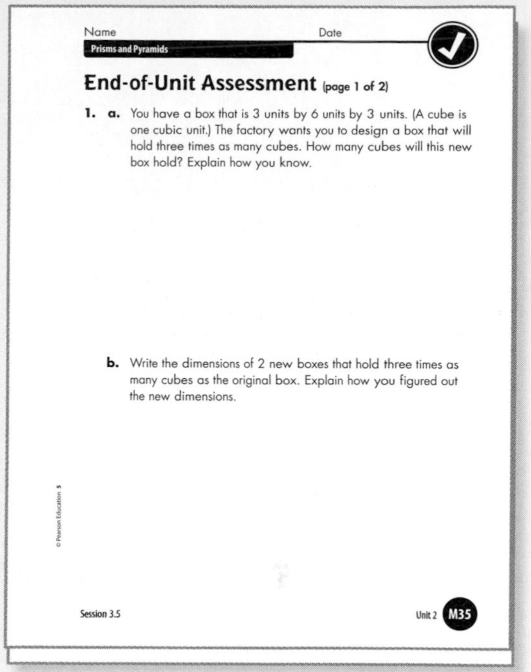

Name Date

Prisms and Pyramids

End-of-Unit Assessment (page 1 of 2)

1. a. You have a box that is 3 units by 6 units by 3 units. (A cube is one cubic unit.) The factory wants you to design a box that will hold three times as many cubes. How many cubes will this new box hold? Explain how you know.

   b. Write the dimensions of 2 new boxes that hold three times as many cubes as the original box. Explain how you figured out the new dimensions.

© Pearson Education 5

Session 3.5 Unit 2 M35

▲ Resource Masters, M35–M36 PORTFOLIO

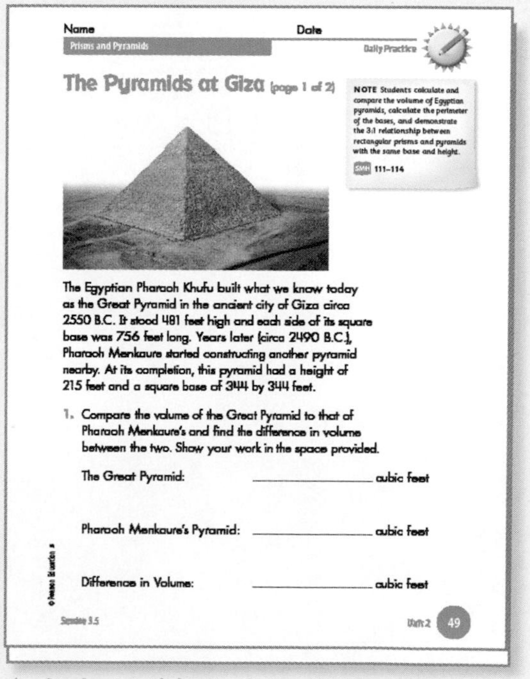

Name Date

Prisms and Pyramids Daily Practice

The Pyramids at Giza (page 1 of 2)

NOTE Students calculate and compare the volume of Egyptian pyramids, calculate the perimeter of the bases, and demonstrate the 3:1 relationship between rectangular prisms and pyramids with the same base and height.

SMH 111–114

The Egyptian Pharaoh Khufu built what we know today as the Great Pyramid in the ancient city of Giza circa 2550 B.C. It stood 481 feet high and each side of its square base was 756 feet long. Years later (circa 2490 B.C.), Pharaoh Menkaure started constructing another pyramid nearby. At its completion, this pyramid had a height of 215 feet and a square base of 344 by 344 feet.

1. Compare the volume of the Great Pyramid to that of Pharaoh Menkaure's and find the difference in volume between the two. Show your work in the space provided.

   The Great Pyramid: ________ cubic feet

   Pharaoh Menkaure's Pyramid: ________ cubic feet

   Difference in Volume: ________ cubic feet

Session 3.5 Unit 2 49

▲ Student Activity Book, pp. 49–50

Professional Development

UNIT 2

Prisms and Pyramids

Teacher Notes

In Part 6 of *Implementing Investigations in Grade 5,* you will find a set of Teacher Notes that addresses topics and issues applicable to the curriculum as a whole rather than to specific curriculum units. They include the following:

Computational Fluency and Place Value

Computational Algorithms and Methods

Representations and Contexts for Mathematical Work

Foundations of Algebra in the Elementary Grades

Discussing Mathematical Ideas

Racial and Linguistic Diversity in the Classroom: What Does Equity Mean in Today's Math Classroom?

Dialogue Boxes

Strategies for Finding the Number of Cubes in 3-D Arrays

For students to determine how many cubes are in a 3-D array, they must mentally construct an image or model of the set of cubes. Students have been observed doing this in a variety of ways, some of which are listed below, in increasing order of the students' ability to see the whole and its parts in an organized manner. You will see your students progress from less organized to more organized methods as the unit advances. However, the progress may be slow, and the same students may approach different tasks with different levels of understanding.

Seeing Arrays as Unstructured Sets

Whether given an actual cube package (e.g., a rectangular prism), a picture of a cube package, or the box that contains that package, some students do not see any organization. In this case, students usually count cubes one by one and almost always lose track of their count. For these students, the task is like counting a large number of randomly arranged objects.

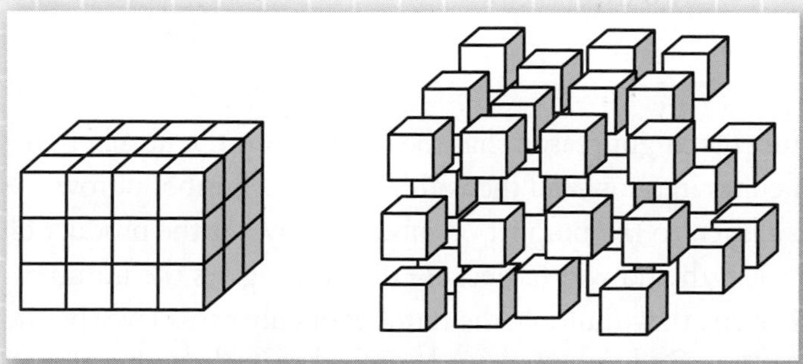

Seeing Arrays in Terms of Sides or Faces

Many students approach 3-D arrays of cubes by thinking only about the sides of the rectangular prism formed by the cubes. These students might count all or some of the cube faces that appear on the six sides. With this method, edge cubes are often counted more than once and cubes in the middle are missed.

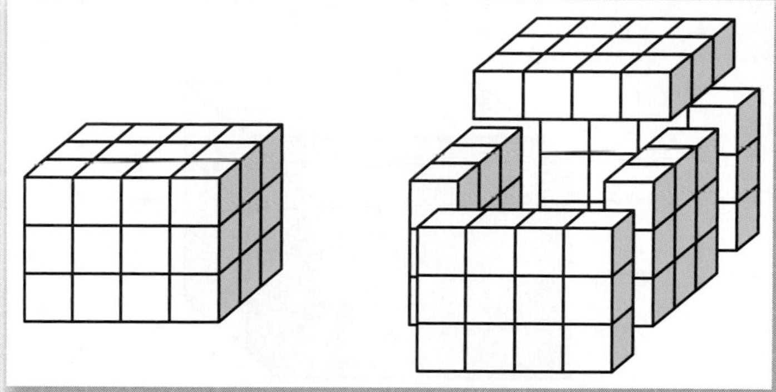

Thus, a box of 36 cubes, $3 \times 4 \times 3$, might be counted as 54 cubes—the front, back, and top each as 12, the right and left sides each as 9.

Most students with this "sides" conceptualization use it consistently, whether they are looking at pictures of boxes, box patterns, or the actual cube configurations. Students who see cube arrays in terms of their faces do not necessarily think of arrays as hollow; they simply think that their method counts all the cubes inside and out.

Seeing Arrays as Having Outside and Inside Parts

Students who take this approach try to count both the outside and the inside of the 3-D array, sometimes doing it correctly but more often incorrectly. They attempt to visualize the entire package and account for each cube.

Correct Counting One student counted the cubes visible on the front face (12) and then counted those on the right side that had not already been counted (6). She then pointed to the remaining cubes on the top, and for each, counted cubes in columns of 3: 1, 2, 3; 4, 5, 6; . . , 16, 17, 18. She then added 12, 6, and 18.

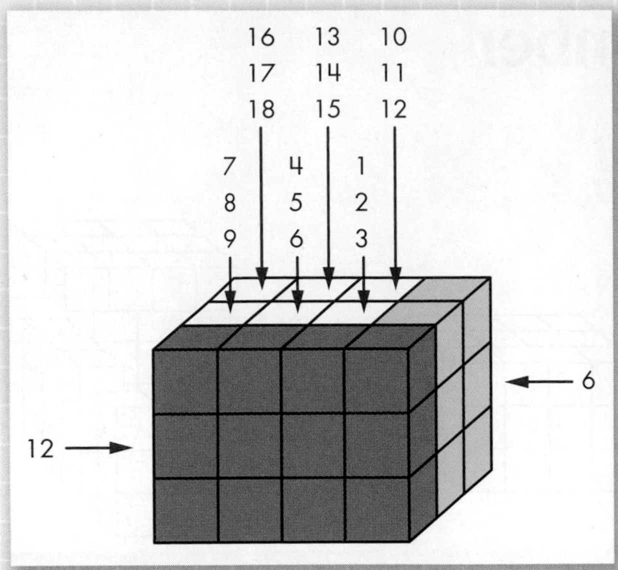

Incorrect Counting One student counted all the outside cube faces of this same array, getting 66. He then said that there were 2 cubes in the middle for a total of 68.

Seeing Arrays in Terms of Rows or Columns

Students count the cubes in successive rows or columns by ones or by skip counting. In the strategy diagrammed below, the student counted 3 cubes for each of the 12 columns.

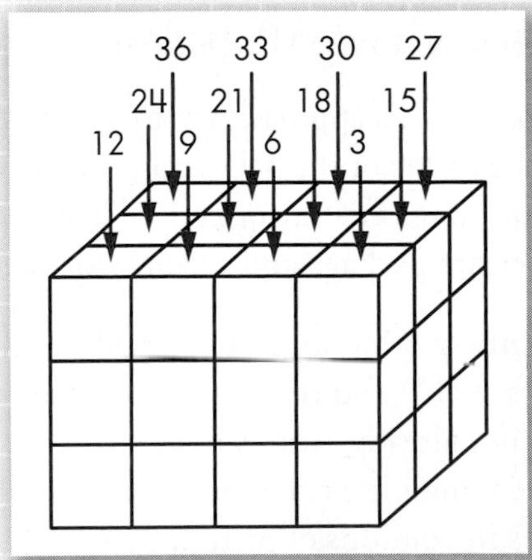

Seeing Arrays in Terms of Layers

Students determine the number of cubes in one layer and then multiply or use repeated addition to account for all the layers. The layers can be vertical or horizontal, and students often use one of the visible faces in a picture as a representation of a layer. Other students look at a box pattern, see the bottom as representing a layer, and then determine the number of layers by looking at the sides of the pattern. Many students who use layering often count the cubes in a layer one by one.

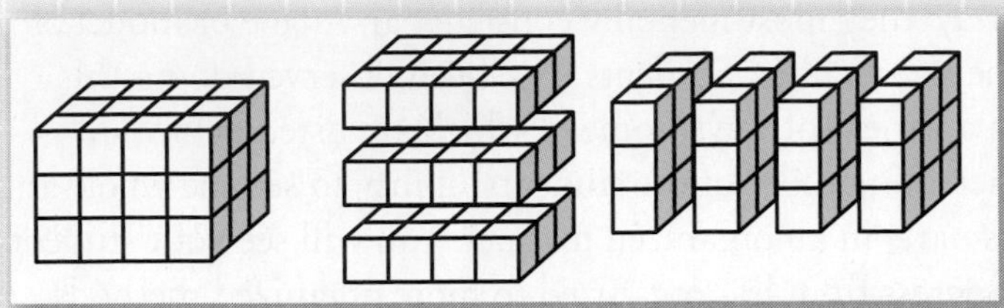

Seeing Arrays as Layers Described by Dimensions

Some students understand how dimensions can be used to describe and count the cubes in an array.

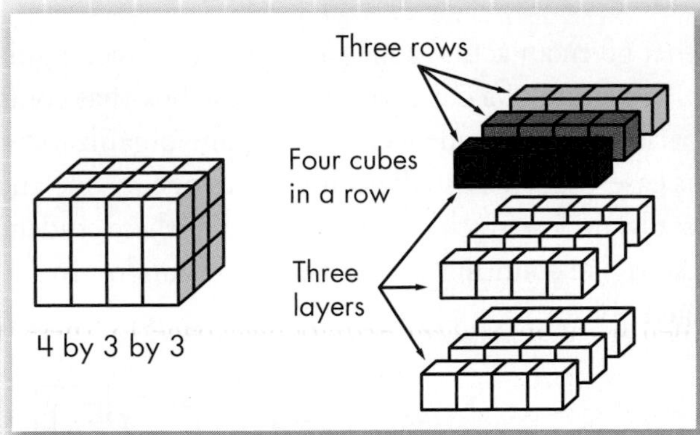

Students might reason that the length gives the number of cubes in a row and the width gives the number of rows in a layer, so the number of cubes in a layer is the product of the length and width. Because the height gives the number of layers, they multiply the number of cubes in a layer by the height to find the total number of cubes in the array. Not all students refer to the dimensions as length, width, and height.

The Learning Process

Students gradually progress to more powerful ways of conceptualizing cube configurations. This is because they have repeated experiences with determining the number of cubes in a box, building boxes, filling them with cubes, counting the cubes, and discussing their ideas with classmates.

Strategies for Finding How Many Packages

To determine how many packages fit in a box correctly, students must accurately visualize the spatial organization of the packages within the box. At first, students may make a variety of mistakes. Through their use of cubes and paper boxes, or by explaining their strategies, they discover their mistakes and why they occurred. Note that this task differs from finding the volume of boxes, because students are not determining the number of single cubic units that fill each box but are instead determining how many *packages* of a given multicube configuration fit inside.

Two useful strategies students often use are these:

- Visualizing where packages fit in a box, often thinking about layers
- Finding relationships between different packages

The following are examples of these strategies and the most common mistakes students make in using them.

Visualizing Where Packages Fit in a Box

For their work on *Student Activity Book* page 15, these three students accurately visualize the organization of Packages A and B within Box 1.

Yumiko: [drawing circles around groups of 4 squares on the bottom of the box picture] 4 here, 4 here, 4 here, 4 here, 4 here, 4 here. There are 6. I can't get any in the top row (layer).

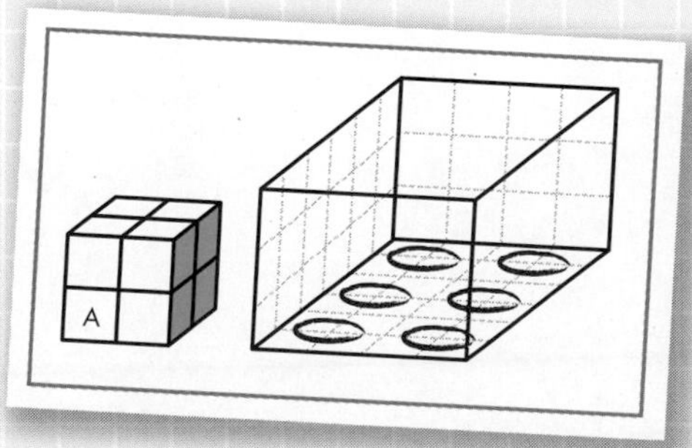

Yumiko's Work

Cecilia: [counting squares on the bottom] So 24 go up.

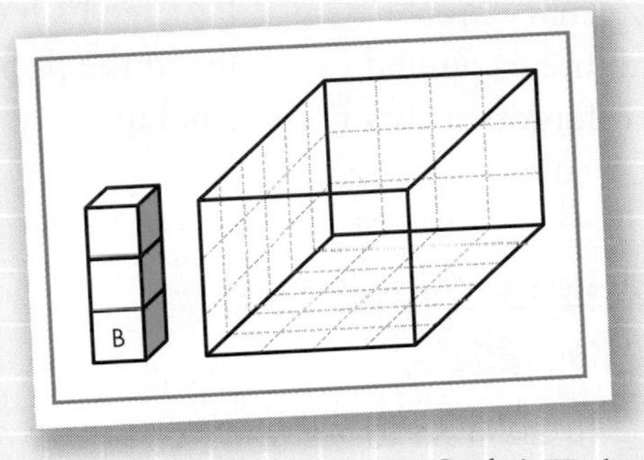

Cecilia's Work

Felix: There are 8 on the bottom and 3 layers, so 24.

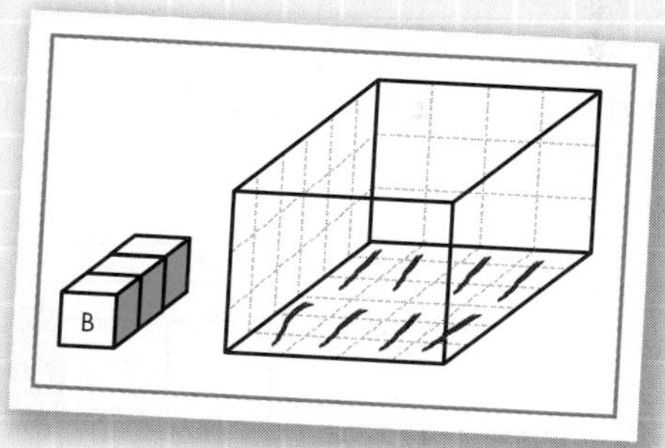

Felix's Work

Avery: I can fit 15 Package Es—5 on the bottom [motioning as indicated in the diagram], times 3.

Actually, only 4 packages fit on the bottom. Package E will *not* fit horizontally along the front.

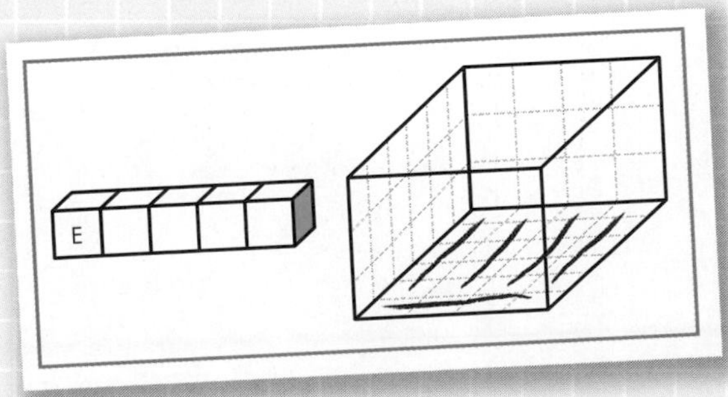

Avery's Work

Another common error is losing track of the original unit.

Zachary: With Package E, there are 20 on the bottom. So 20 × 3 = 60.

Although Zachary properly saw 4 Package Es lying on the bottom, he counted each cube in the packages. Zachary has forgotten that the original unit was a package of 5 cubes.

Finding Relationships Between Different Packages

Comparing different packages (their shape, as well as the number of cubes they are made of) is another strategy that some students use. For example, after finding that 6 Package Ds fit in box 1, Lourdes uses this knowledge in thinking about how many Package Cs fit in the box.

Lourdes: I think 18 Cs, because it's like D. D is three times larger [than C], so it'd be 3 times 6 (for C).

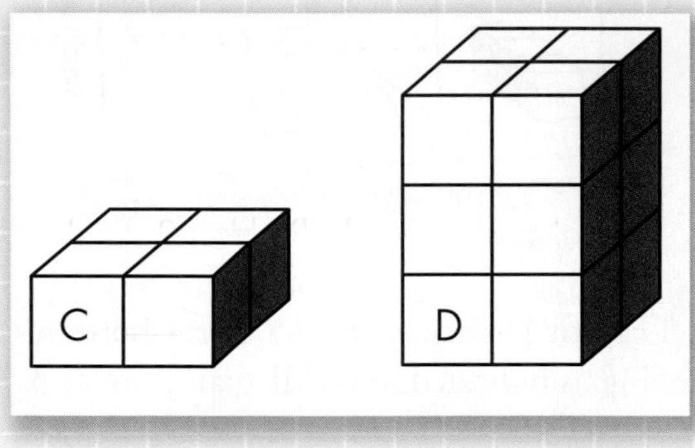

A common mistake that students make when trying to relate different packages is ignoring package organization. These students focus only on number relationships without thinking about how the packages actually fit in the boxes. For example, some students reason that the number of Package Bs that fit in a box is one-third the number of unit cubes. Or, as the following student reasons:

Benito: There are 72 cubes in Box 1, and Package A is made of 8 cubes, so 8 goes into 72 nine times. We can get 9 Package As in this box.

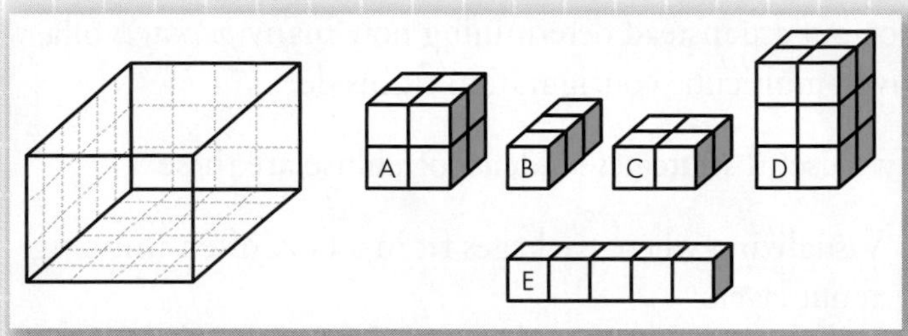

Although this strategy works for Packages B, C, and D with Box 1, it does not work for Packages A or E because copies of these packages do not completely fill the box. This strategy would work if students were allowed to break the packages apart, but they are not.

Assessment: Finding the Volume of Rectangular Prisms

Benchmark addressed:

Benchmark 1: Find the volume of rectangular prisms.

In order to meet the benchmark, students' work should show that they can:

- Accurately find the volume of a rectangular prism when given a two-dimensional representation of the box to hold the prism;
- Clearly explain their solutions.

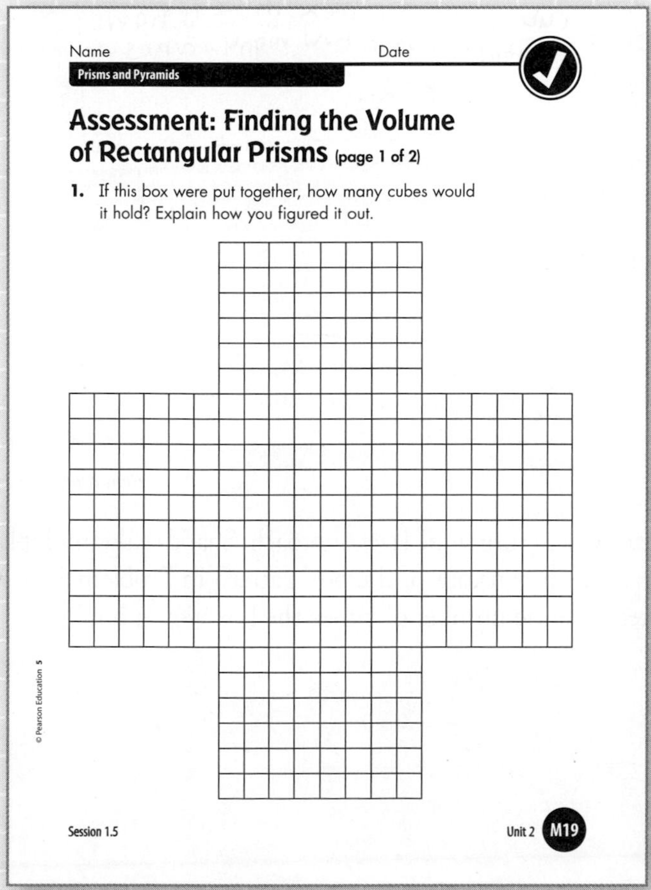
Name Date

Prisms and Pyramids

Assessment: Finding the Volume of Rectangular Prisms (page 1 of 2)

1. If this box were put together, how many cubes would it hold? Explain how you figured it out.

© Pearson Education 5

Session 1.5 Unit 2 M19

▲ Resource Masters, M19

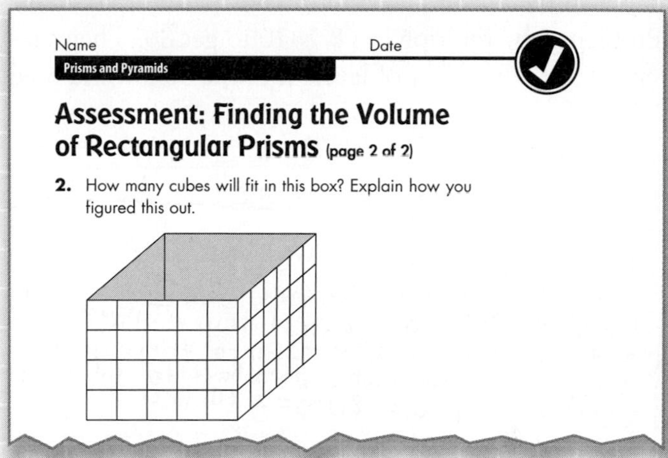
Name Date

Prisms and Pyramids

Assessment: Finding the Volume of Rectangular Prisms (page 2 of 2)

2. How many cubes will fit in this box? Explain how you figured this out.

▲ Resource Masters, M20

Although both problems ask students to find the volume of rectangular prisms, they do so in slightly different fashion. In Problem 1, students need to visualize the box that will result when the pattern is folded. Students may be able to more clearly see the base of the box (the center of the pattern) but may need to determine the height of the box from the sides of the pattern. In Problem 2, the box is pictured as a three-dimensional object. This may make the height of the box easier for some students to see, but the base may be more difficult to determine.

Meeting the Benchmark

These students correctly determine the volume of the boxes shown in the assessment problems. They write explanations that demonstrate their understanding of the relationship between the number of cubes that fill the bottom of the box and the number of layers indicated by the box pattern in Problem 1 or the box shown in Problem 2.

Alternately, they write explanations that demonstrate their understanding of the relationship between the volume of the prism and the length, width, and height of the box.

Nora and Renaldo, for example, both found the number of cubes in the bottom layer of the box pattern pictured in Problem 1 by multiplying 8 × 10 to get 80. They then determined the number of layers that the box would hold.

Nora wrote:

> I think that there are 480 cubes that can fit in this box I figured out that on the first layer there are 80 cubes that fit. Since there are 6 layers I knew that I would have to solve 80X6. I first did 80X3=240. Then I doubled 240 which is 480. That is how I figured out how many cubes are in the box.

Nora's Work

Renaldo wrote:

> I did layers There are 6 layers of 80 so 80X6=480 cubes that fit in the box.

Renaldo's Work

Nora and Renaldo used the same strategy to determine the volume of the box in Problem 2. Nora wrote:

> I Knew that first I had to figure out how much cubes can fit in the first layer of the box, so I solved 5X6 since there are 5 rows on one side and 6 on the other. The answer is 30. So that tells me that there are 30 cubes on the first layer. But there are 4 layers. I did 4X30=120 cubes in the box. That is how I figured out how many cubes in the box.

Nora's Work

Renaldo wrote:

> There are 4 layers of 30 so I did 30X4=120 cubes that fit in the box.

Renaldo's Work

In addition to using the layer approach, Shandra also multiplied the three dimensions of the box pattern in Problem 1 to determine the number of cubes the box would hold.

(Note that the students in Shandra's class use the term *depth* to refer to the dimension from the front to the back of the box.) She wrote:

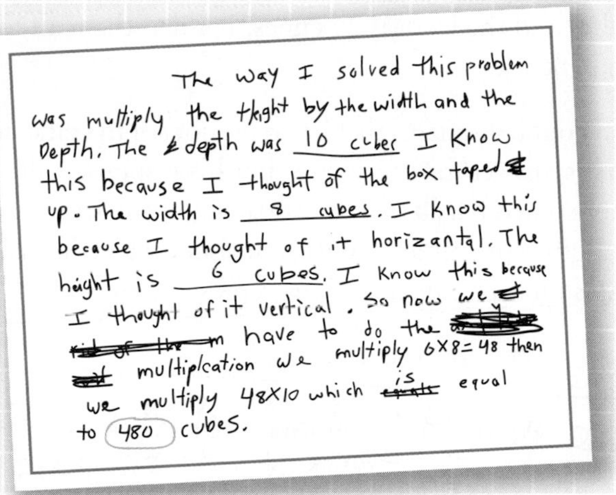
The way I solved this problem was multiply the thight by the width and the Depth. The depth was 10 cubes I Know this because I thought of the box taped up. The width is 8 cubes. I Know this because I thought of it horizantal. The height is 6 cubes. I Know this because I thought of it vertical. So now we have to do the multiplcation we multiply 6X8=48 then we multiply 48X10 which is equal to 480 cubes.

Shandra's Work

Shandra also used this approach to determine the volume of the box pictured in Problem 2. She wrote:

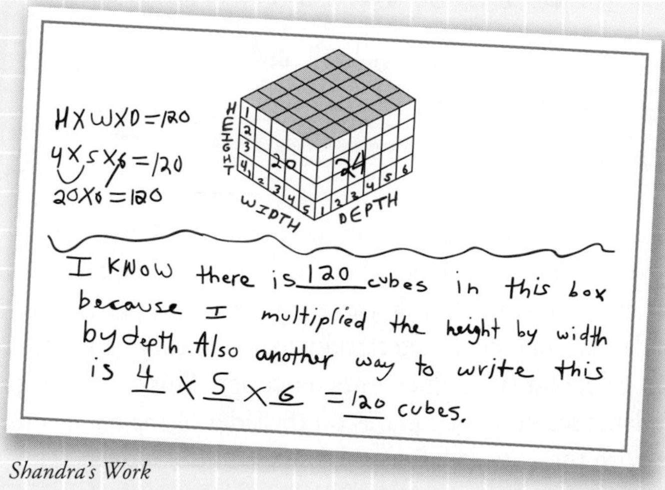
HXWXD=120
4X5X6=120
20X6=120
HEIGHT
WIDTH
DEPTH
20
24
I KNow there is 120 cubes in this box because I multiplied the height by width by depth. Also another way to write this is 4 X 5 X 6 = 120 cubes.

Shandra's Work

Partially Meeting the Benchmark

Students whose answers demonstrate understanding of the structure of the box patterns and the prism that fits inside but who miscalculate the number of cubes partially meet the benchmark. In Problem 1, for example, Olivia correctly determined that there are 80 cubes in the middle (bottom layer) and that the box is 6 layers high. However, when she multiplied 6×80, she came up with an answer of 486.

Ask students like Olivia to look at the box pattern again to check their answers. It is likely that these students can correct their computational error.

Other students may successfully solve one part of the assessment task but not the other. Terrence, for example, was able to find the volume of the open box pattern shown in Problem 1 of the assessment task, but he incorrectly determined the volume of the box show in Problem 2.

In Problem 1, Terrence demonstrated an effective strategy for finding the volume of the box when he first determined the number of cubes in the bottom layer (80) and then multiplied the quantity by the number of layers. He wrote, "I also know that the box's height is 6 so I multiplied 80 six times and got 480."

However, Terrence's attempt to apply this strategy to Problem 2 resulted in an incorrect response. He wrote:

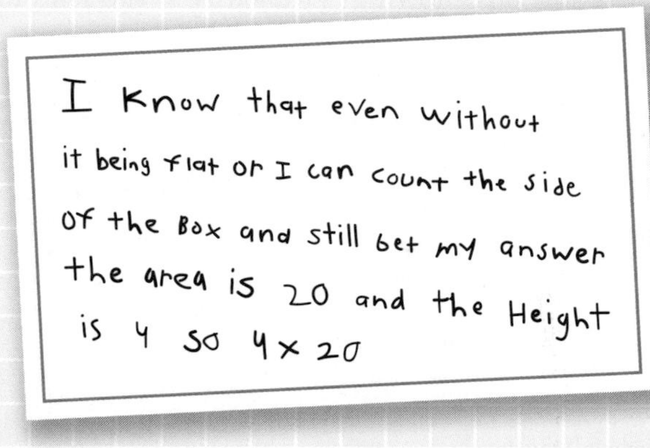
I Know that even without it being flat or I can count the side of the Box and still get my answer the area is 20 and the Height is 4 so 4 x 20

Terrence's Work

Terrence's response to Problem 2 raises questions about his understanding of the structure of rectangular prisms. Because Terrence multiplies the 20 that he sees on the side of the box by the height (or number of horizontal layers) of the box, he does not seem to understand that the 20 represents a *vertical* layer of 20 cubes and that to find the volume he should instead multiply 20 by the number of vertical layers. Ask students like Terrence questions such as these to determine what they do understand:

You said that the side of the box is 20. What does 20 represent? (a layer of 20 cubes) Could the box hold other layers of 20 cubes? How many?

You multiplied 4 × 20 to get your answer. What does the 4 represent? Is 4 the number of layers of 20 that fit in the box? How many cubes fit in the bottom layer of the box? (30) How many layers of 30 cubes could this box hold?

Not Meeting the Benchmark

Some students confuse the volume of the rectangular prism with the number of visible squares that make up the unfolded box pattern. Janet, for example, thought 296 cubes would fit in the box shown in Problem 1 of the assessment question. She wrote:

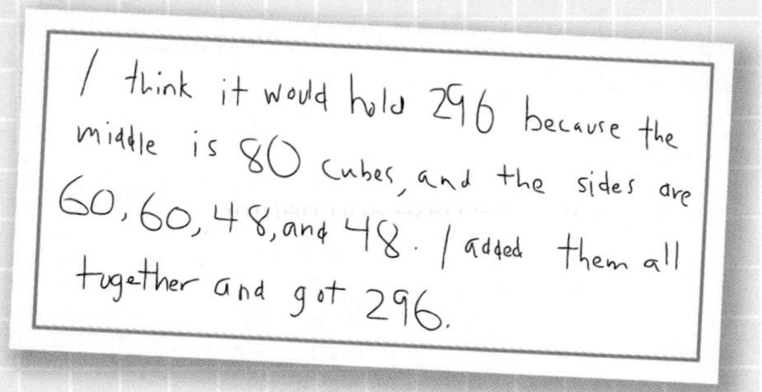
I think it would hold 296 because the middle is 80 cubes, and the sides are 60, 60, 48, and 48. I added them all together and got 296.

Janet's Work

Deon used a similar strategy in Problem 1, but he did not count the squares in the middle of the box pattern. He wrote:

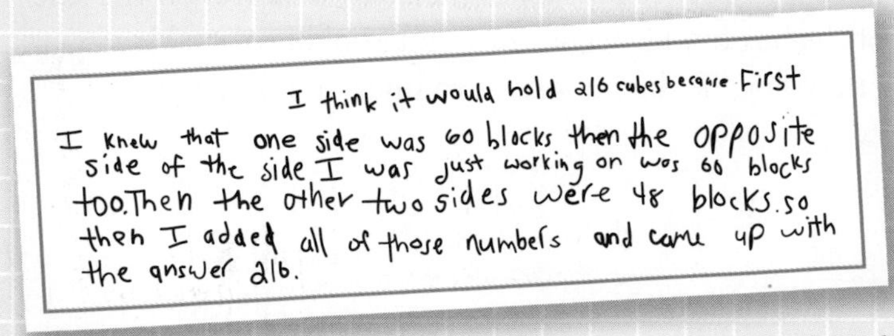
I think it would hold 216 cubes because First I knew that one side was 60 blocks then the opposite side of the side I was just working on was 60 blocks too. Then the other two sides were 48 blocks. so then I added all of those numbers and came up with the answer 216.

Deon's Work

For Problem 2, Janet counted only those squares she could see.

Janet: I think it would hold 44 because the side is 20 cubes and the front is 24 cubes. I added them all together and got 44.

Deon counted squares that he could not see to come up with his answer for Problem 2, but his response still demonstrated a lack of understanding of the structure of rectangular prisms and confusion about what the visible squares on each side of the box represent. He wrote:

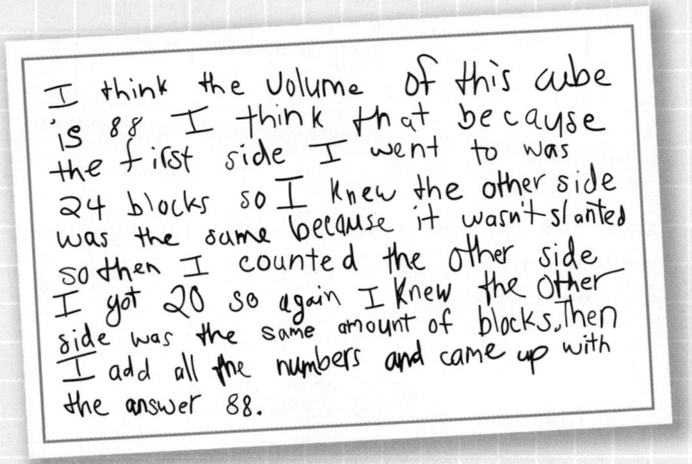
I think the volume of this cube is 88 I think that because the first side I went to was 24 blocks so I knew the other side was the same because it wasn't slanted so then I counted the other side I got 20 so again I knew the other side was the same amount of blocks. Then I add all the numbers and came up with the answer 88.

Deon's Work

Students like Janet and Deon need additional experiences to help them understand what the squares in the box pattern represent. Provide these students with patterns made with one-centimeter grid paper that they can cut out, fold, and fill with centimeter cubes. This should help students see how the squares on the sides of the pattern line up with the outside faces of the cubes in the rectangular prism and that the number of rows of squares on the side represent the number of layers in the prism. Also, ask students to consider the reasonableness of their answers. Are there cubes they cannot see? Are they accounting for all the cubes?

Strategies for Designing Boxes

In their work on *Student Activity Book* page 27, students use a variety of strategies to generate possible dimensions for boxes that hold Packages A–D. Most students seem to need some type of concrete material to generate or test their ideas—cubes to make the packages or grid paper to make box patterns.

Using Packages

Many students generate ideas by stacking packages. Martin and Stuart found that 6 worked as one dimension because they could stack copies of any of Packages A–D and get a package that was 6 cubes high.

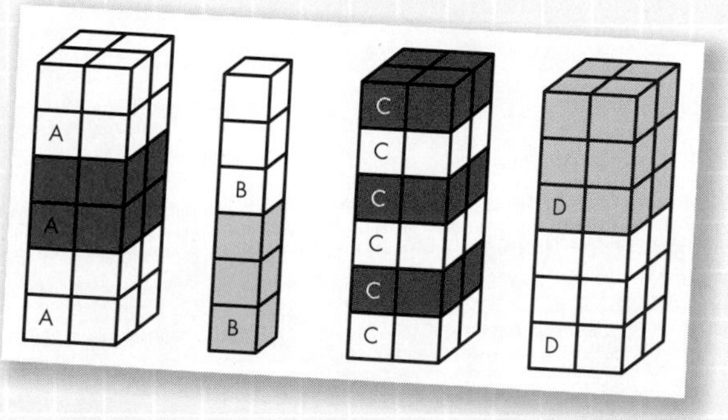

Hana and Samantha also used packages to generate ideas. They put together *different* packages in various combinations to help them think about the problem. For instance, they put together one A, one C, one D, and two Bs in the configuration shown here.

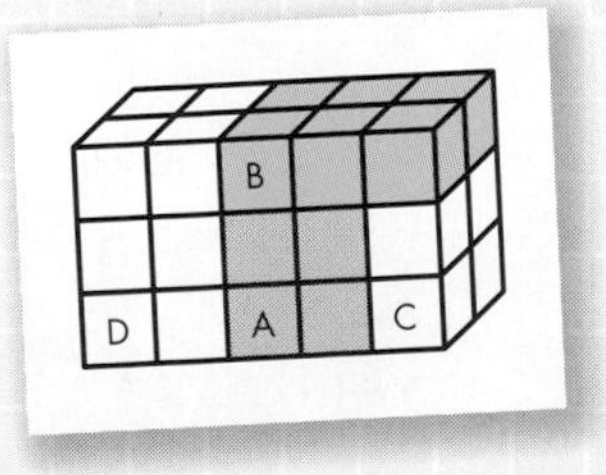

Hana tried to see whether Package A would fill a box shaped like the one pictured here by placing Package A in various positions alongside the configuration.

Hana: This won't work. It won't fit; there's extra space.

The girls then made a new configuration and tested it by placing As alongside.

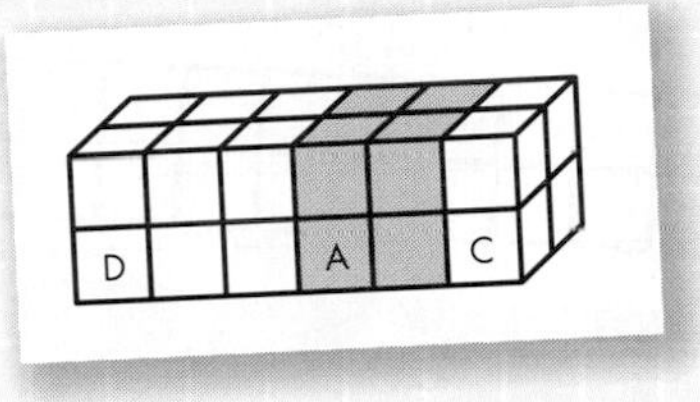

Samantha: Four Bs here and four Bs here; that's 8. And six Cs. We got it!

Using Patterns

Deon and Alex think that a box 6 × 6 × 6 will work for Packages A–D. They draw a pattern for such a box on graph paper. They then test this box by trying to visualize how many of each package will fit.

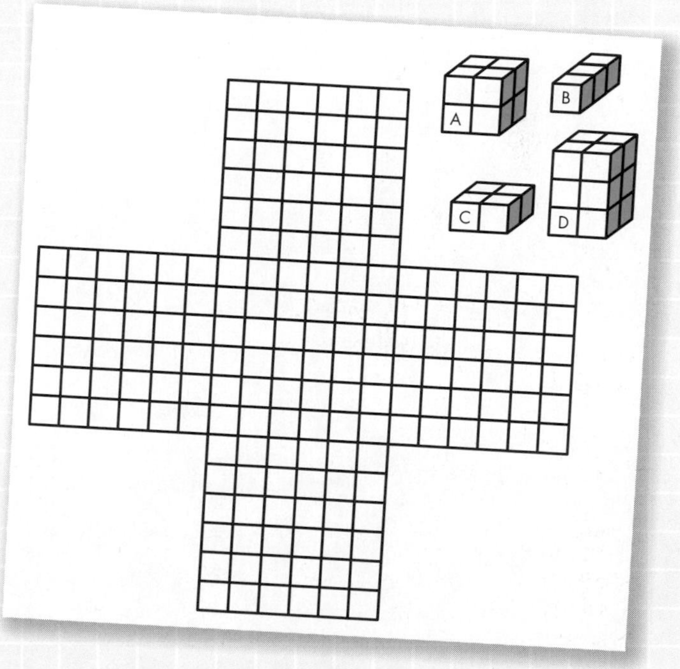

Using Numbers

Some students generate possible dimensions for boxes by thinking about numbers. They are exhibiting an emerging knowledge of the concept of numerical factors.

Nora proposes that a box 12 × 2 × 2 might work.

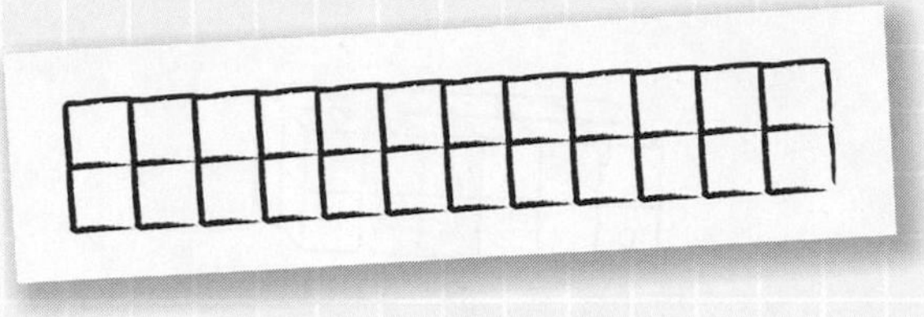

Nora: [Moving a single Package A along a 12 × 2 rectangle she has drawn on graph paper] 2, 4, 6, 8, 10, 12. That fits. Now for Package B—3 fits into 12. That's 3, 6, 9, 12. [She checks her answer by moving Package B along a 12 × 1 strip on her rectangle.] That's one (12 × 1) row, then I could put another row here (beside it), and here and here (above the previous 2). And Package D works because I just showed 3 fits into 12. And C works because there are 3 Cs in a D.

Notice that as Nora's work progresses, she relies more and more on manipulation of numbers rather than packages: "D works because I just showed 3 fits into 12." The connections she is establishing between numerical and spatial ideas lay an excellent foundation for the concepts of factors and divisibility.

Strategies for Measuring Space in the Classroom

Students can meaningfully determine how many cubic meters fit in their classroom by visualizing the repeated placement of cubic meters throughout the room. For example, they might repeatedly place a single meterstick end to end along the wall, imagining the cubic meters projecting out from the wall. Be sure to ask students what they are doing; determine whether they are imagining cubes or simply measuring the wall's length. Other students might actually want to repeatedly place a cubic meter model along one wall, making the row of cubes more concrete.

The examples below illustrate the complexities that students often introduce into this task.

Converting Cubic Centimeters to Cubic Meters

Tavon and Stuart use the concrete blocks in the wall to find the number of centimeters in the length, width, and height of the classroom. They reason as follows:

- 1 block = 21 cm high. The height of the room is 15 blocks, so the height of the room is 21 × 15 = 315 cm.
- 1 block = 40 cm long. One wall is 28 blocks long, so the length of this wall is 40 × 28 = 1,120 cm.

Similarly, they find the width of the room to be 810 cm. They then multiply the three dimensions together on the calculator, getting 285,768,000.

Stuart: To get cubic meters, just divide our last answer by 100.

Tavon: Why divide by 100?

Stuart: Because there are 100 centimeters in a meter.

After hearing the boys' conversation, the teacher takes several cubic centimeters and drops them into the meterstick model of the cubic meter as the boys watch.

Teacher: Do you think 100 of these [cubic centimeters] fill one of these [the cubic meter]?

Stuart and Tavon: No!

Teacher: How about converting your original measurements to meters?

Tavon: I think that would be better.

The boys then correctly change each of their original measurements into meters and multiply them to find the number of cubic meters in the classroom. If the teacher had suspected that they would have difficulty converting centimeters to meters, she could have had them remeasure the room in meters rather than centimeters.

As it frequently happens with students of this age, when Tavon and Stuart tried to convert one volume unit to another, they only thought about the relationships between the corresponding length units. They did not properly visualize how many cubic centimeters fit in a cubic meter. The teacher redirected the students from trying to convert cubic centimeters to cubic meters, to directly determining the volume of the room in cubic meters.

Converting Blocks to Meters

Alex, Zachary, and Lourdes find the dimensions of the room in meters by noticing that there are 5 horizontal blocks ("bricks") for every 2 meters. They count the number of blocks in the length and width and then convert these block measurements to meters.

Alex: (For the length) 30 bricks $\div$ 5 = 6, and 6 $\times$ 2 = 12 meters. (For the width) 20 bricks $\div$ 5 = 4, and 4 $\times$ 2 = 8 meters. So 8 $\times$ 12 = 96 square meters on the floor.

The students find that 5 blocks high make 1 meter, and they determine from this that the height of the room is 3 meters. They multiply the dimensions together and get 288.

Teacher: What are the units?

Alex: Meters.

Zachary: Square meters.

Lourdes: Cubic meters.

Alex and Zachary: Right. Cubic meters.

Teacher: Do you think that 288 of these cubic meters [pointing to the cubic meter model] will fit in this room?

Alex: That's an awful lot.

Lourdes: I don't know.

Teacher: Why don't you make a model of the classroom to see whether your answer makes sense?

The students decide that a connecting cube will stand for one cubic meter, and then they build the 4 walls of the classroom with cubes. This model convinces them that they are correct.

Alex: Look how many cubes we have already and we don't even have the middle filled.

Teacher: I know that another group got 240 cubic meters. What do you think?

The three students decide that maybe somebody measured wrong. They ask the teacher what the other group's measurements were.

Teacher: They measured the room as 3 by 8 by 10 meters.

Lourdes: It's either that we counted wrong, or that they counted wrong.

The students recount the blocks several times, getting a variety of answers—28, 29, and 30. Finally, they recount the blocks together very carefully, getting 30.

Lourdes: The other group counted wrong. We recounted a zillion times. We think the length is 12 meters.

Although Alex, Zachary, and Lourdes' approach contained some good mathematical thinking, their solution track was indirect; they had many questions to resolve.

- They used blocks in the walls to find the number of meters rather than measuring in meters directly.
- They had to think about what the unit of measure was called.
- They had to make a model to convince themselves that the magnitude of their answer was reasonable.
- They had to remeasure the length several times to convince themselves that their answer was correct and that the other students' answer must be wrong.

This struggle to make personal sense out of their procedures was essential for these students. The teacher asked questions that encouraged them to reflect more on what they had done and to clarify their thinking.

Teacher Note

Student Methods for Comparing Containers

The structure of the first activity in Investigation 3, Comparing Volumes of Containers, is intentionally informal to give students the opportunity to devise their own strategies for comparing the relative volumes of household containers of different shapes.

To test their answer, most students directly compare 2 containers by pouring rice from one container into another.

Comparison Strategies

Expect to see variation in how students place the containers in order before measuring with rice or sand. One often-used strategy is to visualize or try fitting one container into another and then to compare leftover space. For example:

- This container fits into this one.
- The space around the edges and the heights are the same, but one fits into the other, so that one is bigger.
- If you put this into there, there's room left over.

Another common strategy is to analyze shape characteristics of the containers and focus on particular dimensions to compare. For example:

- These two (cylinders) are the same [pointing to the bases], but this one is higher.
- This one is shorter in height, but wider in width.
- This is a lot taller, but this one is a ton wider.

Verifying Answers

Students might pour from a smaller container to a larger container and see that the larger container is not filled. They also might pour from a larger container to a smaller and see it overflow. In either case, they usually draw the correct conclusion.

Students might also use one container to judge the other two. For example:

- Two of the small boxes fill the jar. About 1 large box fills the jar. So the jar is the biggest.
- When we pour the rice from the jar into the toothpaste box, it comes up to here. But when we pour rice from this bottle into the box, it only comes up to here (lower than the jar). So the jar has more room.

Students may also use less accurate methods. For example:

- We counted the number of handfuls of rice that fit in each container.

These students had a good idea in that they chose a unit of measure (handfuls) to compare the containers. The problem is that their handfuls were not all equal, so their measurements were quite inaccurate. Choices such as these provide good opportunities to talk with students about the need for standard units of measure.

Geometric Solids and Their Parts

A geometric *solid* is a shape that has three dimensions—length, width, and height. In mathematics, unlike everyday conversation, these geometric shapes are called "solids" whether they are filled or hollow. There are many types of geometric solids. Some, including spheres, cones, and cylinders, have some curved surfaces. Others, called *polyhedra,* have only flat surfaces. Two common types of *polyhedra* are prisms and pyramids.

Prisms

The solids we call prisms have two parallel, congruent faces that are connected by rectangular regions. Either congruent face can be called the base. For a rectangular prism, naming one face the base is arbitrary. Therefore, it is common to simply identify the face that the prism is resting on as the base. Bases are shaded in the diagram.

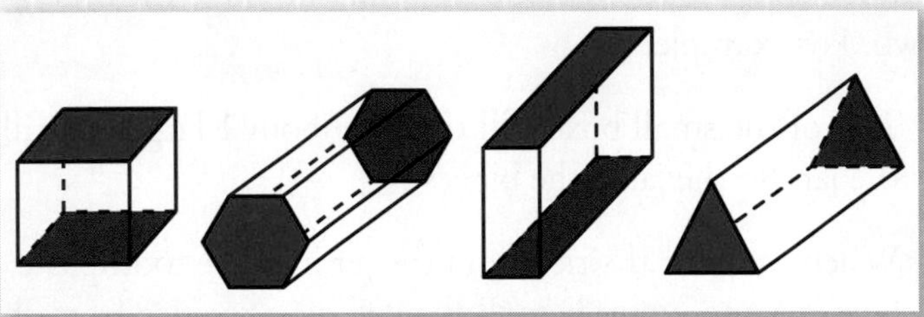

To define prisms in their own words, students might say, "Prisms have a top and bottom that are the same shape and sides that are all rectangles." Of course, this description is accurate only when the prism is standing on one of its bases.

Pyramids

A pyramid is a three-dimensional object. One face, often called a base, is a polygon. The other faces are triangles, which meet at a point. The line segments, which connect the top point to each vertex of the base polygon, are called edges. Students might describe a pyramid as having "a flat bottom and a pointed top with sides that are all triangles."

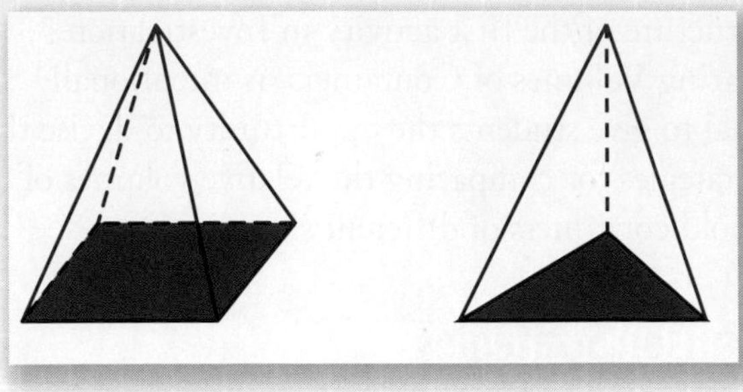

Cylinders

Like a prism, a cylinder has two congruent faces called bases. Unlike a prism, the bases of a cylinder are circles and not polygons. Because the bases are circles, a cylinder does not have polygonal faces; it has a curved surface connecting the circular bases.

Cones

The relationship between a cylinder and a cone is analogous to that between a prism and a pyramid. A cone has one base, which is a circle, and a curving surface, which comes to a point.

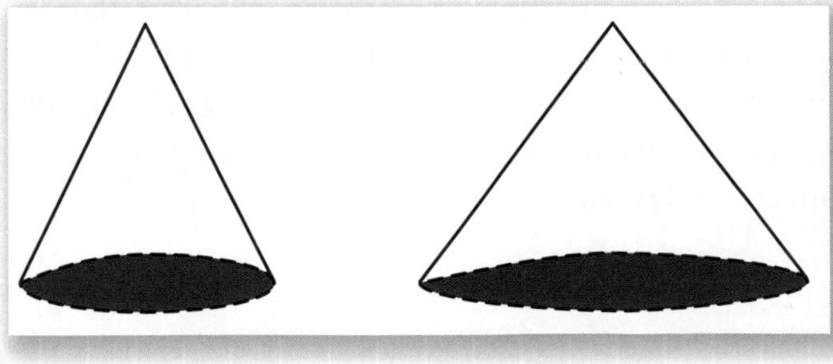

Height and Diameter

The *height* of a pyramid or cone is the length of a perpendicular line segment drawn from the top to the base. The height of a prism or cylinder is the distance from base to base. The *diameter* of a cone or cylinder is the length of a segment that has its endpoints on the circular base and passes through the center of the base.

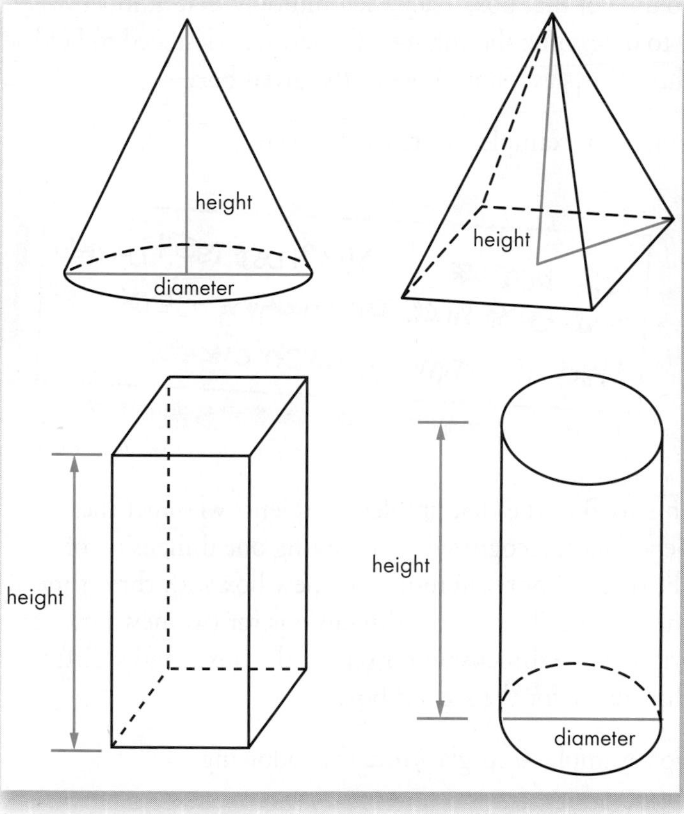

Some students may confuse the length of an edge or side of a pyramid or cone with its height. This is incorrect but will not be far off for tall, narrow solids. As such figures become flatter (see diagram), the inaccuracy of using the wrong dimension for height will increase.

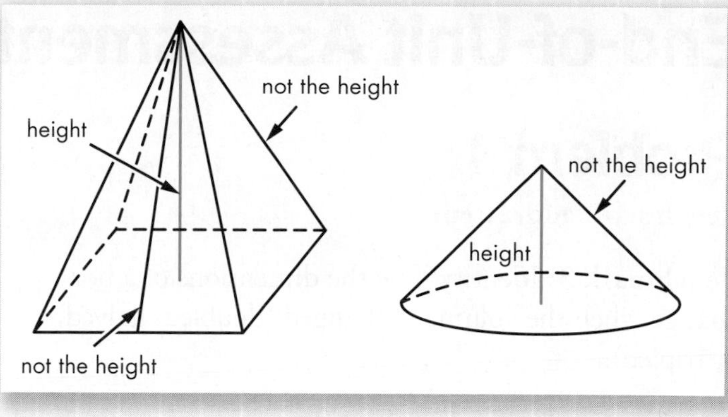

Other Terminology

As students talk about solids, they will use various words to describe their parts and even the figures themselves. For example, in talking about a rectangular prism, they may refer to *corners* instead of *vertices* and *sides* instead of *faces.* They may call the figure a *box* instead of a *rectangular prism.* It is important for students to use words that communicate their meanings clearly. Students have used the correct mathematical terms in Grades 3 and 4 and are expected to use them in Grade 5. Encourage the use of these standard terms by using them consistently and expecting students to do the same.

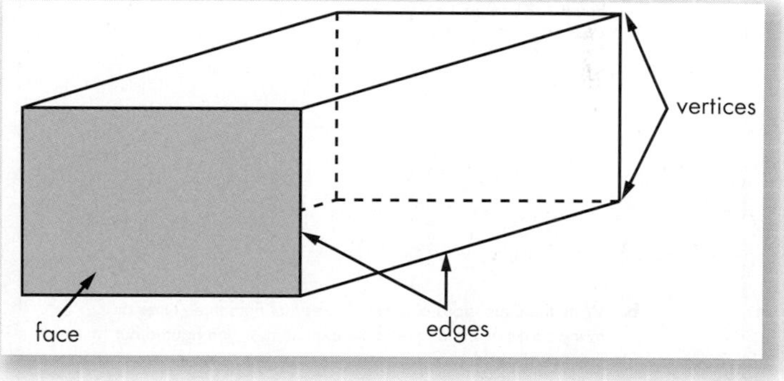

Teacher Note

End-of-Unit Assessment

Problem 1

Benchmark addressed:

Benchmark 3: Identify how the dimensions of a box change when the volume is changed (doubled, halved, or tripled).

In order to meet the benchmark, students' work should show that they can:

- Determine the volume of the new box with three times the volume, given the dimensions of the box;
- Accurately determine dimensions for two new boxes with triple the volume of the given box and explain their strategies for doing so.

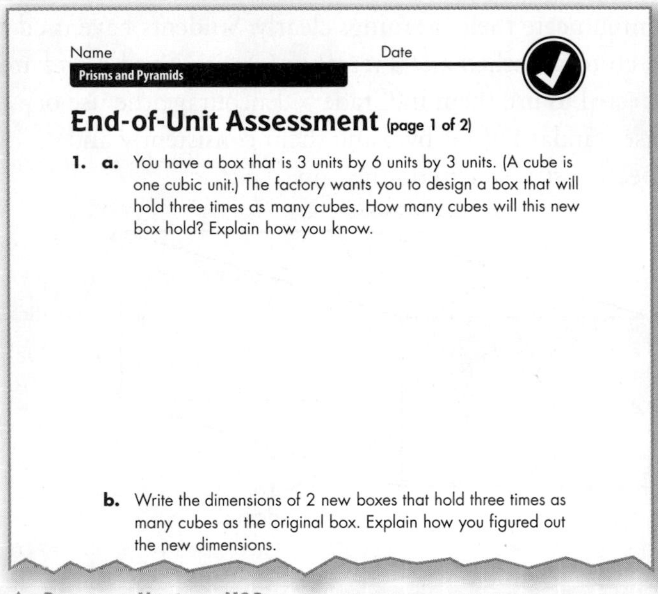

Name Date

Prisms and Pyramids

End-of-Unit Assessment (page 1 of 2)

1. a. You have a box that is 3 units by 6 units by 3 units. (A cube is one cubic unit.) The factory wants you to design a box that will hold three times as many cubes. How many cubes will this new box hold? Explain how you know.

b. Write the dimensions of 2 new boxes that hold three times as many cubes as the original box. Explain how you figured out the new dimensions.

▲ Resource Masters, M35

Meeting the Benchmark

Students who meet the benchmark accurately answer both parts of Problem 1. In Part A, these students are likely to use the dimensions of the original box to determine the volume of that box. They then multiply that number by 3 to determine the volume of a new box designed to hold three times as many cubes as the given box.

Janet, for example, wrote the following:

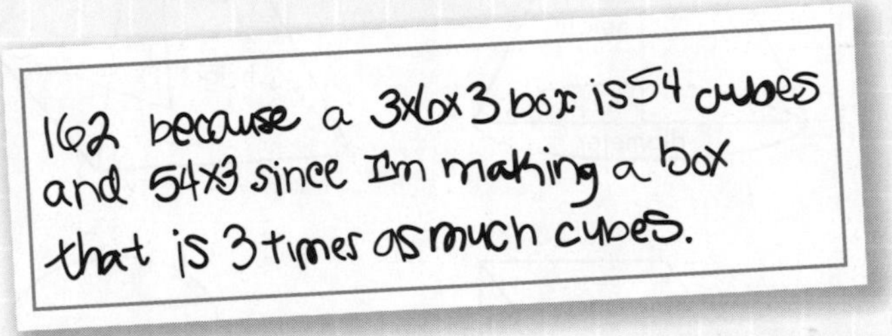

162 because a 3x6x3 box is 54 cubes and 54x3 since I'm making a box that is 3 times as much cubes.

Janet's Work

In Part B of the first problem, students who met the benchmark recognized that tripling one dimension of the original box will result in a new box with three times the volume. They wrote dimensions for two new boxes by tripling one dimension for one of the boxes and a different dimension for the second box.

For example, Georgia wrote the following:

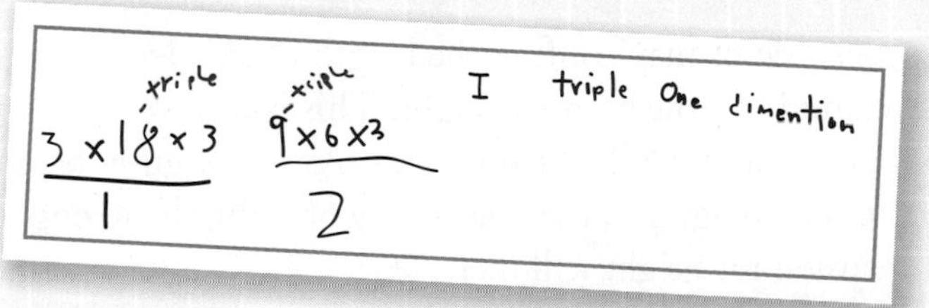

triple triple
3 x 18 x 3 9 x 6 x 3 I triple One dimention
1 2

Georgia's Work

Other students who meet the benchmark may determine the dimensions for two new boxes by using cubes to build three $3 \times 6 \times 3$ rectangular prisms, like the prism that will fill the original box. These students then put the three prisms together in different configurations (as in the figure below) and record the dimensions of each new prism that results.

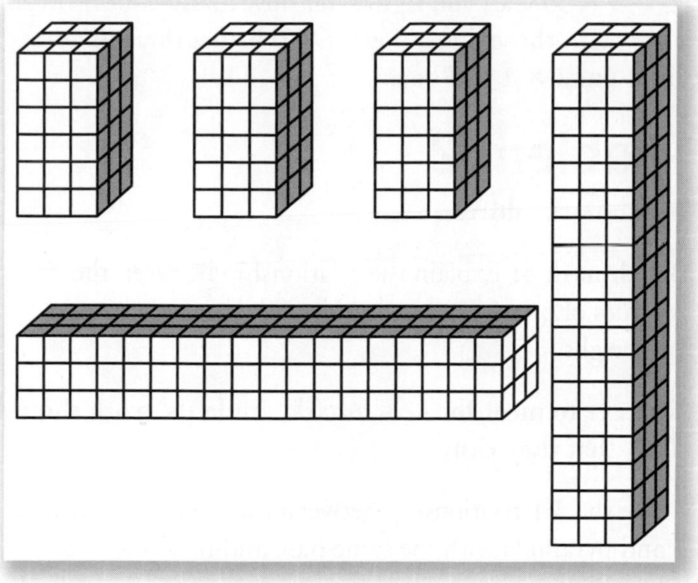

Felix, for example, recorded the dimensions 18 × 3 × 3 and 6 × 3 × 9 and wrote:

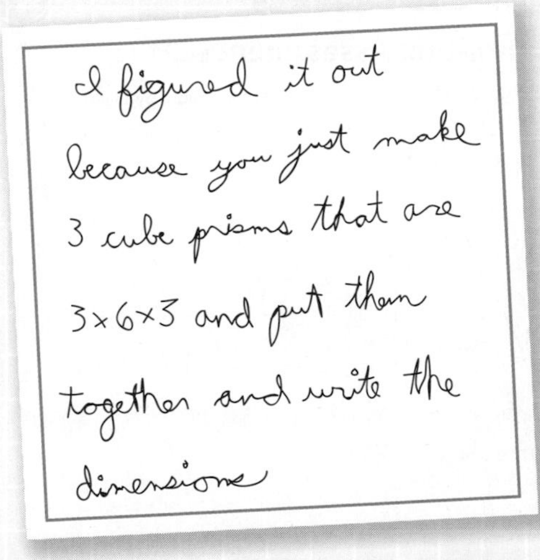

I figured it out because you just make 3 cube prisms that are 3×6×3 and put them together and write the dimensions

Felix's Work

Although students like Felix meet the benchmark, their strategy is not as efficient as that of students who recognize that tripling one dimension will result in a box with triple the volume of the original box. To help students like Felix recognize this relationship, ask them what they notice about the original dimensions and the new dimensions.

You started with a 3 × 6 × 3 box and wrote dimensions for two boxes to hold three times as many cubes. Let's look at the dimensions of your new boxes. How are the dimensions different from those of the original box? What changed? What stayed the same?

Partially Meeting the Benchmark

Students who partially meet the benchmark are able to find the volume of a box when given its dimensions, but they may not answer both parts of Problem 1 accurately.

Students who partially meet the benchmark also may make computation errors in the first part of Problem 1, while still demonstrating understanding of the relationship between the volumes of the original box and the new box. Charles, for example, multiplied 3 × 6 × 3 to determine the volume of the original box, but he wrote 56 as the volume instead of 54.

He understood that he needed to multiply the volume of the original box by 3 to determine the volume of a box to hold three times as many cubes. However, he came up with an incorrect answer of 168 cubes.

Other students who partially meet the benchmark may write accurate dimensions for only one new box instead of two in Part B of Problem 1. Question these students to see whether they were unable to come up with a second response or simply misread the question. Ask them to explain how they arrived at their correct response and how they can use that strategy to create a second box.

You said that if you triple one dimension, you end up with a box that holds three times as many cubes. You tripled the 6 and got the dimensions 3 × 18 × 3. What would happen if you tripled a different dimension? Would that also create a box that would hold three times as many cubes?

You built three 3 × 6 × 3 prisms with cubes and put them together to make a 6 × 3 × 9 prism. Then you wrote those dimensions down. Is there a different way that you can put the 3 × 6 × 3 prisms together to come up with dimensions for a second box?

Not Meeting the Benchmark

Students who do not meet the benchmark may have no correct response in Problem 1 or may respond correctly to Part A, but fail to have at least one correct response in Part B.

Alex, for example, correctly determined the volume of the original 3 × 6 × 3 box, but did not answer the question about the volume of a box designed to hold three times as many cubes. Question students like Alex to see what they do understand.

I see that you came up with 54 as your answer for Part A. What does the 54 stand for? Which box will hold 54 cubes? Can you read the question again? What do you know about how many cubes the new box will hold?

In Part B, Alex does triple the volume of the original box to get 162 but fails to write dimensions for two new boxes. However, his writing indicates that he may have built and stacked prisms containing 54 cubes.

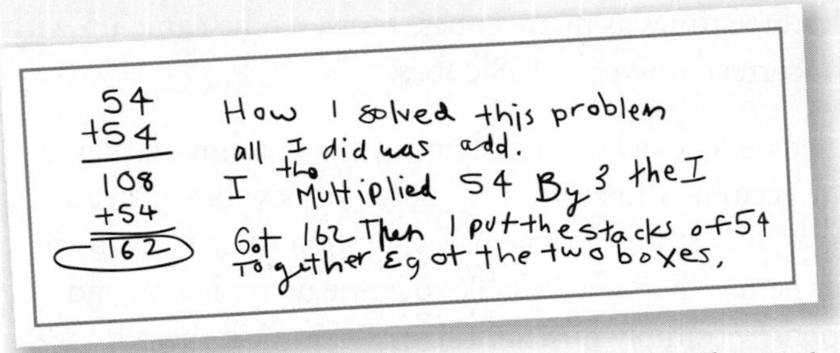

Alex's Work

Ask students like Alex to demonstrate what they did and ask questions to help them connect their cube structures to the dimensions of the two new boxes.

Other students write dimensions (e.g., 9 × 18 × 9) that reflect their belief that to triple the volume of a box, it is necessary to triple every dimension. Help these students consider the effect of tripling all three dimensions. Start with a box with a small volume, (e.g., 2 × 1 × 3).

What's the volume of this 2 × 1 × 3 box? How many cubes would fit in a box designed to hold three times as many cubes as this one? *(18)* If we tripled all of the dimensions of the 2 × 1 × 3 box, what would they be? *(6 × 3 × 9)* Can you figure out how many cubes will fill a box with those dimensions? *(162)* Is that three times as big as our 2 × 1 × 3 box?

Problem 2

Benchmark addressed:

Benchmark 4: Explain the relationship between the volumes of prisms and pyramids with the same base and height.

In order to meet the benchmark, students' work should show that they can:

- Use the 3:1 relationship between the volume of prisms and pyramids with the same base and height to explain how to find the volume of the pictured square pyramid.

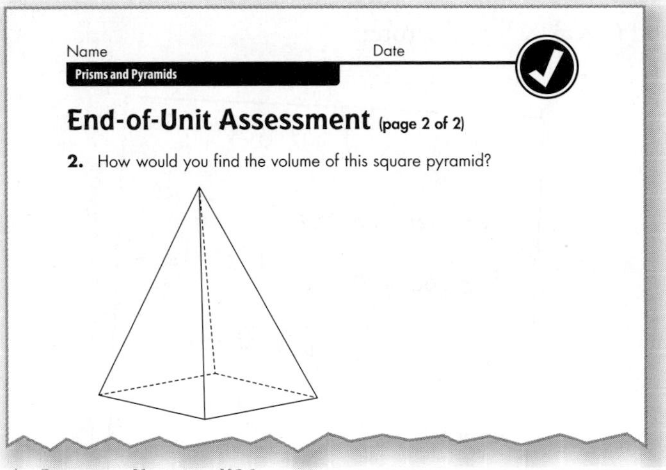

▲ Resource Masters, M36

Meeting the Benchmark

Students who meet the benchmark understand that prisms and pyramids with the same base and height have a 3:1 volume relationship. They recognize that they can find the base (length × width) and height of the pyramid, determine the volume of the related square prism by multiplying the base times the height, and then divide the resulting number by three to determine the volume of the pyramid.

Georgia demonstrated understanding when she wrote this:

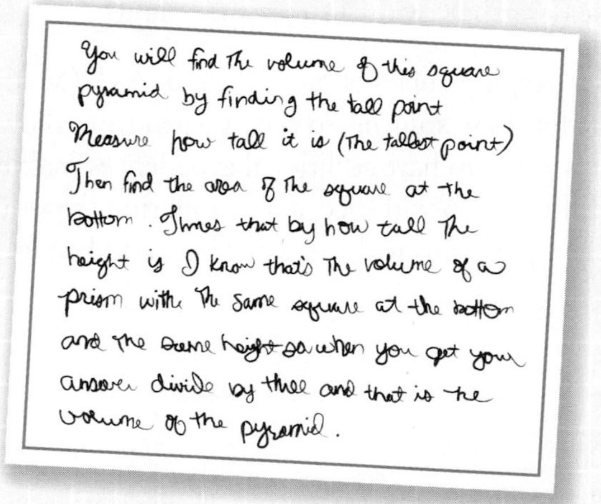
You will find The volume of this square pyramid by finding the tall point Measure how tall it is (The tallest point) Then find the area of The square at the bottom. Times that by how tall The height is I know that's The volume of a prism with The same square at the bottom and The same height so when you get your answer divide by three and that is the volume of the pyramid.

Georgia's Work

Partially Meeting the Benchmark

Students who partially meet the benchmark understand that there is a relationship between the volume of the square pyramid and the square prism with the same base and height but may be unsure of that relationship.

Avery, for example, recognized that the volume would have to be less than the volume of the square prism but mistakenly thought that the volume of the pyramid was half rather than one third the volume of the prism. He wrote:

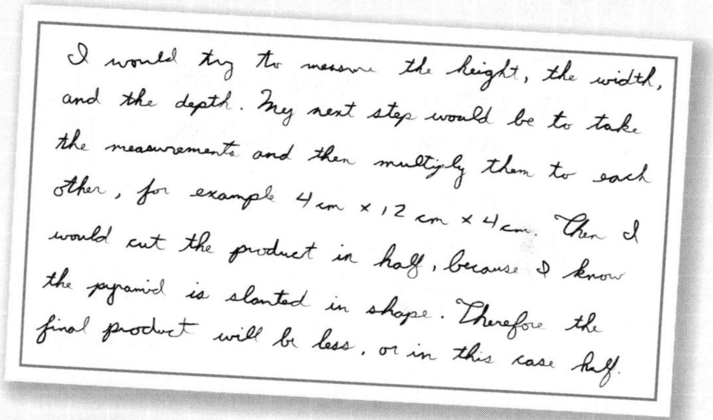
I would try to measure the height, the width, and the depth. My next step would be to take the measurements and then multiply them to each other, for example 4 cm × 12 cm × 4 cm. Then I would cut the product in half, because I know the pyramid is slanted in shape. Therefore the final product will be less, or in this case half.

Avery's Work

Ask students like Avery to think about work they did with finding the volume of related pairs of geometric solids in Investigation 3. Do they remember the relationship between how much rice it took to fill the pyramid and how much rice it took to fill the prism with the same base and height; the rice it took to fill the cone and the cylinder with the same base and height, and so on?

Not Meeting the Benchmark

Students who do not meet the benchmark may use the formula for determing the volume of a prism to explain how they would find the volume of the square pyramid without recognizing that the pyramid's volume must be less than that of the related prism.

Janet, for example, wrote:

> You would measure the area (length X width) of the base. Then you would measure the height of one of the sides. You times the area by the height of the sides and that is the volume of the pyramid.

Janet's Work

Note: Janet's response also indicates possible confusion about how to measure the height of the pyramid because she refers to the height of "one of the sides" rather than the height of the pyramid measured in a perpendicular line from the base to the highest point. Provide students like Janet with a pyramid from a set of geometric solids and ask them to demonstrate how they would determine the height.

Ask students like Janet how they would determine the volume of a square prism with the same base and height as the square pyramid. Then ask questions to help them consider whether the volume of the two solids could be the same.

What if we had a square prism that has the same base as this pyramid and exactly the same height? How would you find the volume of that prism? What if we filled both the prism and the pyramid with rice? Which would have the greater volume? In other words, which would hold more rice? Can we find the volume of both by multiplying the base (length × width) times the height?

Consider keeping copies of *Solid Patterns A–K* (M26–M30), available for these students to access when time allows. This will allow them to have additional experiences making these solids, filling them with rice, and comparing the volume of prisms and pyramids with the same base and height.

Understanding Multiplication and Arrays

In this classroom, many students are finding the volume of the boxes by using a layer approach (the number of cubes in a layer times the number of layers), and some are beginning to discover that they can find the volume by multiplying the dimensions of the box (length × width × height). One student, Nora, consistently determines the number of cubes in 3-D arrays by using a layer strategy. She has also discovered that the number of cubes can be found by multiplying the three dimensions. But as her class discusses these strategies, Nora is puzzled about counting the cubes—she thinks that cubes are being double- or triple-counted. Even though almost every student in the class has discovered and is routinely employing a layer approach, not one of them has an immediate answer to Nora's confusion.

Nora: The corner cube gets counted once when you find the length, once for the width, and once for the height. So the answers we're getting should be wrong. But I think they're right.

To simplify the problem, the teacher shows a one-layer array of cubes, 4 by 3.

Teacher: How many cubes do you see here?

Terrence: There are 12. 4 times 3.

Nora: I know that the answer is 12, but when you multiply, you count the corner cube once for the length and once for the width. So you count it twice.

Martin: That cube is both the length and the width. It's okay to count it twice.

The teacher separates the cubes into three rows of 4 and points to the cubes in one row.

Teacher: 1, 2, 3, 4. What am I counting here?

Lourdes: Cubes.

Teacher: [Pointing to the three rows] 1, 2, 3. What am I counting here?

Nora (excitedly): Rows of cubes. You're not counting cubes this time. So first you count cubes, then you count rows.

Lourdes: So you're not really counting the cubes twice. We got it!

The teacher reconfigures the 4 by 3 array of cubes and adds two more 4 by 3 layers.

Teacher: What are the dimensions of the cube array I just made? How many cubes are there in this rectangular prism?

Zachary: That's easy. We already figured out that there are 12 cubes in the bottom layer. There are three layers now, so it's 3 times 12. That's 36.

Teacher: Some of you have said that you can multiply the length times the width times the height to find the number of cubes in a 3-D array. Does what Zachary just said help you understand why that works?

Nora: I can really see it now! You multiply the length times the width to get the bottom layer. That's 4 times 3 equals 12. The prism is three layers high, so then you can multiply by 3 to find how many cubes there are altogether. That's length times width times height.

Deon: It's like what we just said about first counting cubes in one row and then counting how many rows there are. Now we're just figuring out one layer and then we're multiplying by the number of layers.

Teacher: Nora was worried about counting the corner cube more than once when we multiply the length times the width times the height. Was she right? Are we counting the corner cube more than once when we do that? Is that a problem?

Yumiko: Martin said before that the corner cube is part of the length and the width so it's okay to count it twice. It's part of the height, too, so it's okay to count it more than once.

Martin: When we count it again for the height, we're just finding out how many layers there are.

Nora's question about counting the corner cube more than once posed a real challenge for her classmates. They were sure that multiplying the length times the width gave the number of cubes in a one-layer rectangular array. But initially, not all students recognized what they were counting; they were applying multiplication mechanically. After the teacher breaks the problem down for the students by separating the array into three rows of four, students are able to justify the procedure by saying that they are multiplying the number of cubes in a row by the number of rows to determine the total number of cubes in the layer. In addition, the teacher realizes that, although many students are also convinced that multiplying the length times width times height gives the number of cubes in a multilayer array, some also apply this procedure mechanically. By adding two more layers to the original array, she helps them see and articulate why this procedure works.

Common Student Strategies for Doubling

During Session 1.3, students work on *Student Activity Book* page 11. They are trying to find dimensions for a box that has double the volume of a 2 × 3 × 5 box. The teacher is watching and interacting with students as they think about this problem. The teacher knows that all students need opportunities to test their ideas concretely by using patterns and cubes, and she also wants to encourage them to think about how the original dimensions are changed to double the volume. She knows that students will work more with this idea in Sessions 1.5 and 1.6. The teacher stops to watch Olivia and Walter, who are working together on this problem.

Olivia and Walter make a box that is 2 × 3 × 5 and fill it with a 2 × 3 × 5 package of cubes.

Walter: We have to double the number of cubes, so I think we should double each dimension. So what would the new dimensions be?

Olivia: 4 × 6 × 10.

Walter: [looks at the prism they have made] So right now it's 2 high, we need to make it 4 high.

The students add cubes. Walter turns the prism onto its side so that it is now three cubes high.

Walter: Now we have to build this side up, so it's 6 high.

Teacher: You're trying to double the number of cubes, right? How could you figure out how many cubes are in the original cube package by looking at the dimensions?

Walter: The bottom layer would be 6, and there would be 5 layers, so it's 30.

Teacher: What would twice that many be?

Olivia: 30 doubled is 60.

Teacher: So you're making a box now that is 4 × 6 × 10. How many cubes would that be?

Walter: The bottom layer would be 4 × 6, that's 24. And 10 layers would be 240. Wow!

Olivia: That's way too many. It's a lot more than doubled. I think we did something wrong.

Teacher: Maybe it would help if you go back and look at the first box you built. Try to use it to help you think about a new box that holds twice as many cubes.

Olivia and Walter begin working again, and the teacher moves on to watch other students. She asks Tavon how he doubled the number of cubes.

Tavon: I knew that it needed to be 60 cubes. I kept drawing patterns until I found one that held 60 cubes. I know that it's double because I filled it with 60 cubes.

Teacher: What are the dimensions of your new package? Do the new dimensions have anything to do with the dimensions of the original box? Or would the dimensions of the original box help you figure out how to double the number of cubes?

The teacher leaves Tavon to think about this, and moves on to Shandra and Janet.

Shandra: I made two packages of cubes that were 2 × 3 × 5. I put them next to each other and that made a package that was 4 × 3 × 5. Then Janet noticed what I was doing and said that I could put them together another way.

Janet: So we put them together and made a new package that was 2 × 6 × 5. And then the last way we did it was a package that was 2 × 3 × 10.

The two students demonstrate the three different positions for their two packages.

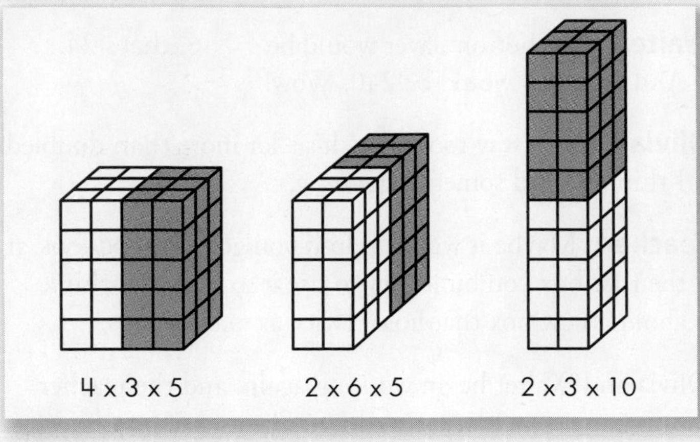

Teacher: That's interesting. What do you notice when you compare the dimensions of your new boxes with those of the original box? What if the original box were $3 \times 3 \times 5$? Do you think you could figure out a way to double the number of cubes without actually building the packages and putting them side by side? I bet you could!

As the teacher circulates around the room, she initially encourages students to think about the problem spatially—asking students how they can use the cubes or the box patterns to help them determine dimensions for a new box that holds double the number of cubes. She notices that Olivia and Walter are focusing only on the dimensions and redirects them to think about the total number of cubes. To encourage Janet and Shandra to think more abstractly about the problem, she asks them to think about how the dimensions of the original box changed when they made the new boxes and then gives them a new doubling problem to solve.

Talking About Units of Volume

After the activity, Building Models of Volumc Units, these students are describing and comparing the different volume units they have built. As they consider what makes a unit a cube, they discuss the difference between square and cubic units. They consider, as well, the factors that determine the name of each cubic unit.

Teacher: What is a cube?

Tamira: A square!

Teacher: A square?

Tamira: It's like a number cube. It's got 6 faces.

Teacher: Is there anything special about those 6 faces?

Tamira: It's like if you put square blocks on them.

Teacher: What makes this a cube? Or what doesn't make it a cube?

Renaldo: On that [pointing to the cubic foot], the faces are all equal to each other, and on that [indicating a cement block in the classroom wall], they aren't.

The teacher holds up, for comparison, a square made from four 12-inch rulers and a cubic foot.

Teacher: How would you describe these?

Yumiko: One's a square and one's a bigger square (the cube).

Teacher: Yumiko, how is a cube different from a square?

Yumiko: This one (the cubic foot) you can see everything inside of it. It is more like a cube. And that (the square foot) is more like an outline of it (the cubic foot).

Teacher: So is this [holds up cubic foot] like a cube, or is it a cube?

Yumiko: It is a cube.

Teacher: If you wanted to talk about these with somebody else, what would you call them?

Charles: That's a cubic foot and that's a square foot.

Joshua: If I wanted the three-dimensional square, I'd say, can I please have a cubic foot. If I wanted this [holding up the square], I'd ask for the two-dimensional square.

Walter: This should be called a cube, and this should be just called a square. Because you know how you have those little cubes of ice, you don't call those squares, you call them cubes.

The teacher now stands next to a cubic meter and a cubic yard that students have made. She places a cubic foot, a cubic inch, and a cubic centimeter where all students can see them.

Teacher: Would everyone agree that these are all cubes?

Various Students: Yes. That's right.

Teacher: How are these cubes different? How can you tell someone which cube you are using?

Nora: That one is 1 foot. That one is 1 inch.

Teacher: So how should I name these different cubes when we are talking about them?

Hana: We should tell how big they are. Like a foot cube, or a meter cube.

Teacher: So to help us understand what cubic units we're talking about, we agree to tell how big they are, the way Hana did. Mathematicians call a "foot cube" [pointing to the model] a cubic foot, and a "meter cube" a cubic meter, so these are the terms we'll be using.

In this discussion, the teacher asks questions that help students understand the difference between square and cubic units of measurement.

Choosing a Volume Unit to Measure the Classroom

In Session 2.2, students make models of a cubic inch, foot, yard, centimeter, and meter to create a visual image of the three dimensions of these measurements and to think about choosing appropriate units for measuring. In this discussion students are deciding which of these units would be appropriate for measuring the volume of a large space—their classroom.

Teacher: Now that you've built and compared these units of volume, which do you think would be good units to use for measuring the amount of space in the classroom? Explain why you think that.

Alex: Centimeters.

Teacher: Do you mean centimeters or cubic centimeters?

Alex: Oh yeah. We could measure the dimensions with centimeter rulers, but we would be figuring out how many cubic centimeters would fill the room.

Janet: I think cubic feet would be better—they're bigger. You wouldn't have to count up all of the little centimeter cubes.

Felix: I agree. Cubic centimeters are really small. I bet it would take millions of them to fill this room.

Teacher: What do people think about what Janet and Felix are saying? Do you agree with them? Can you use an example to explain why you agree?

Cecilia: I was thinking that it's like what we did last week when we filled a box with different packages. You could fit more of the small packages in the box. Remember, 24 Package Bs fit in the box and only 6 Package Ds.

Alex: Yeah. Now that I think about it, it would take a really long time to measure this room with centimeter cubes because there would be so many.

Teacher: So does the class agree that a cubic foot would be better to use than a cubic centimeter? [Students indicate agreement.] Are there any other units that would be good to use?

Deon: We could use cubic meters. They're bigger than the cubic feet so there would be even less of them to keep track of.

Rachel: One group made a cubic yard and it was almost the same as the cubic meter, so it would be good too.

Martin: Maybe we could use both.

Teacher: You're right that they would both be good units to use. However, after you measure, you need to compare your answers with other groups' answers. Would it be a problem if some students used cubic yards and some used cubic meters?

Tamira: We'd have different answers, so it would be hard to tell whether anyone made a mistake.

Mitch: Right. I think that if we're going to compare our answers, we all need to use the same thing.

In this classroom, students articulate an important factor that influences which units they should use to measure a large space—that larger volume units (cubic feet, cubic yards, cubic meters) are more efficient to use to than smaller units (cubic centimeters, cubic inches). The teacher checks for understanding and agreement among all students in the classroom by asking for examples that support their thinking. In addition, when students suggest that more than one unit could be used to measure the classroom, she asks how that would affect students' ability to compare results.

Dialogue Box

Exploring the Three-to-One Relationship

In Session 3.2, this class has been working with the paper solids shown on *Student Activity Book* page 39. After the students have compared the volume of the solids in each pair with rice, the teacher places a set of paper solids on a table. She has written the answers that students have agreed on in a large chart on the board.

Pair	Solids	Number of Smaller Solid Needed to Fill Larger Solid
1	A, B	3
2	C, D	3
3	E, F	3
4	G, H	2
5	I, J	6
6	I, K	3

Teacher: As you worked with these pairs of solids, what did you find?

Zachary: One of the two in each pair has a point.

Shandra: And the other one in the pair has a flat top.

Alex: The smaller one ends in a point.

Lourdes: The bigger ones are bigger cause they go up [motioning along 2 vertical parallel lines with her hands] and the smaller ones come together [making a point with her hands].

Mitch: It looks like in pairs 1, 2, 3, and 6, the bigger one had three times the rice as the smaller one. Pairs 4 and 5 were different.

Teacher: What was special about the solids that have the three-to-one relationship?

Tavon: In pair 4, the point (the top of the cone) is higher. In the others (other pairs), the points are even; they're the same.

Olivia: The heights are the same, except for pair 4.

Renaldo: They all fit inside each other, so they're even in height.

Lourdes: When the heights were the same, the straight ones were three times bigger.

Teacher: Some of you have talked about the heights of these solids. What does height mean?

Olivia moves to the table and places her hand horizontally across the tops of both solids in each of the first three pairs and pair 6.

Olivia: They're the same height here, they're the same height here, here, and here.

Teacher: What do we define as height on these shapes—from where to where?

Hana: The base [she holds out a horizontal hand] to the top of the object [moves her horizontal hand upward].

Teacher: You said the heights are the same for the solids that are three-to-one. Is that the only thing that's the same?

Yumiko: If you look at the bases, if you put them together [motions with her hands], they are the same shape.

Teacher: Are you saying that the bases of the rectangular prism and rectangular pyramid [points to pair 1] are exactly the same size?

The teacher first holds the two solids with their square bases facing the students and then places the prism on top of the upside-down pyramid so that their bases fit together.

Tamira: Yes, the bases are the same. Exactly the same.

Teacher: What about pair 2 [showing their bases]? Are the bases of these the same?

Students: Yes!

Teacher: How would you prove that the base has something to do with the three-to-one relationship?

Rachel: Look, the bases are the same for shape I and shape K, but shape J is different. And the heights are the same shape. Shape I didn't have three times the rice as shape J.

Teacher: So the height isn't enough?

Terrence: No, they have to have the same base.

The teacher moves from general comments about what students notice about the pairs of solids to a specific discussion about the three-to-one relationship. While she was interacting with students as they worked, she specifically asked Mitch to share his observation about the three-to-one relationship and called on him after several other students shared their observations. She pushes students to define height, wanting students to notice that, although the height of a prism is the same as a length of an edge, the same is not true of the height of a pyramid. Finally, she wants students to notice and realize that both the base and height of related solids have to be the same for the three-to-one relationship to exist.

Student Math Handbook

The *Student Math Handbook* pages related to this unit are pictured on the following pages. This book is designed to be used flexibly: as a resource for students doing classwork, as a book students can take home for reference while doing homework and playing math games with their families, and as a reference for families to better understand the work their children are doing in class.

When students take the *Student Math Handbook* home, they and their families can discuss these pages together to reinforce or enhance students' understanding of the mathematical concepts and games in this unit.

Math Words and Ideas

Rectangular Prisms

Math Words
- rectangular prism
- three-dimensional (3-D)

A geometric solid is a figure that has three dimensions—length, width, and height.

A rectangular prism is one type of geometric solid. (See other examples of geometric solids on pages 111–114.)

Here are some examples of real-world objects that are shaped like a rectangular prism.

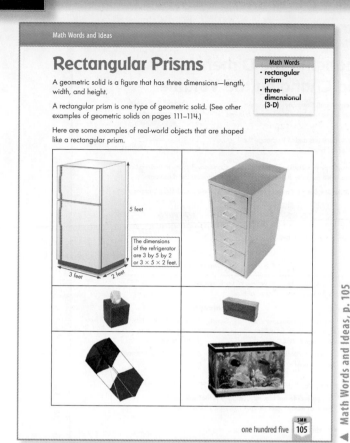

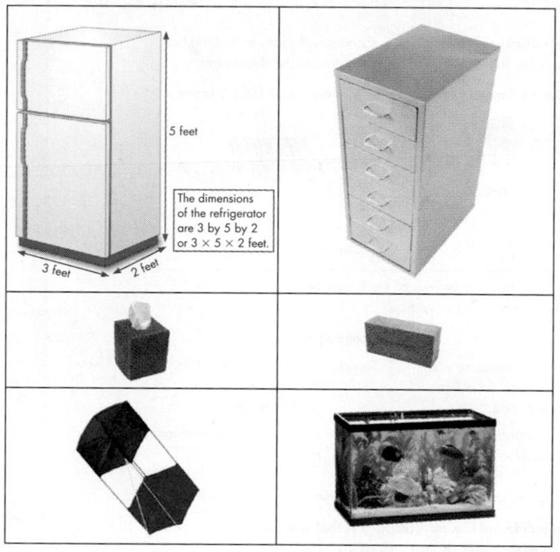

one hundred five SMH 105

▲ Math Words and Ideas, p. 105

Math Words and Ideas

Volume of Rectangular Prisms (page 1 of 2)

Math Words
- volume

Volume is the amount of space a 3-D object occupies. You can think of the volume of a box as the number of cubes that will completely fill it.

Both Olivia and Joshua solved this problem about the volume of a box.

How many cubes will fit in this box?

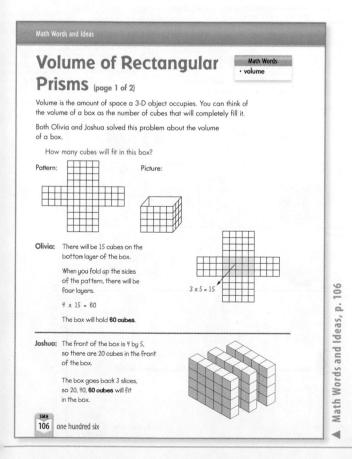

Pattern: Picture:

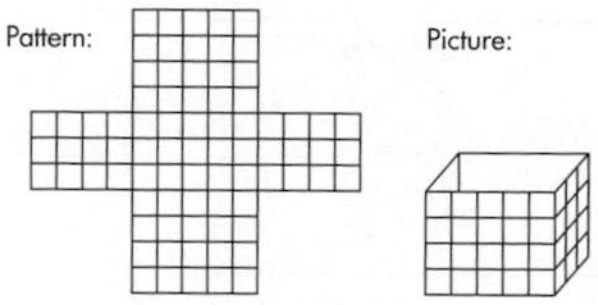

Olivia: There will be 15 cubes on the bottom layer of the box.

When you fold up the sides of the pattern, there will be four layers.

4 x 15 = 60

The box will hold **60 cubes**.

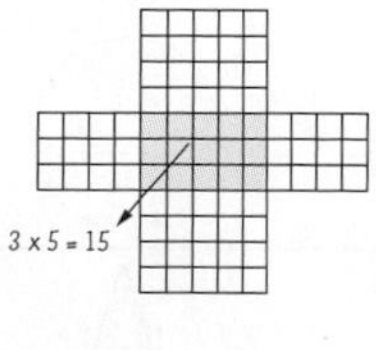

Joshua: The front of the box is 4 by 5, so there are 20 cubes in the front of the box.

The box goes back 3 slices, so 20, 40, **60 cubes** will fit in the box.

SMH 106 one hundred six

▲ Math Words and Ideas, p. 106

Math Words and Ideas

Volume of Rectangular Prisms (page 2 of 2)

Martin solved this problem: The bottom of a box is 12 units by 5 units. The box is 8 units high. What is the volume of the box?

Martin's solution
The bottom layer of the box will have 60 cubes because 12 x 5 = 60.

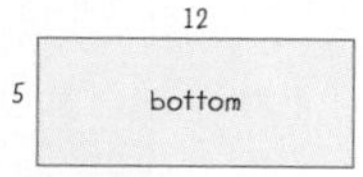

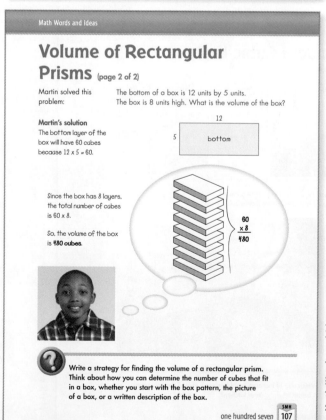

Since the box has 8 layers, the total number of cubes is 60 x 8.

So, the volume of the box is **480 cubes**.

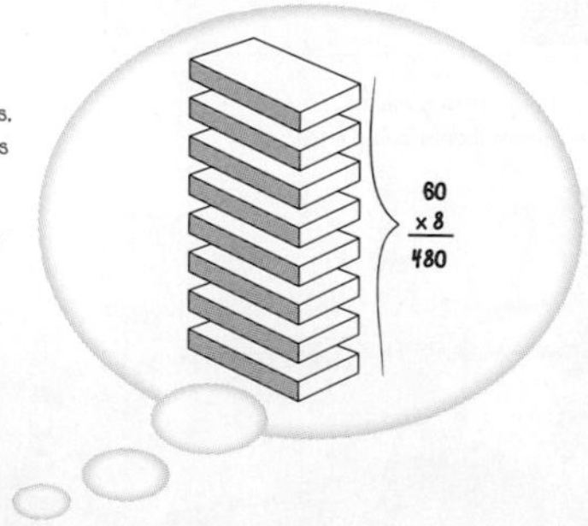

Write a strategy for finding the volume of a rectangular prism. Think about how you can determine the number of cubes that fit in a box, whether you start with the box pattern, the picture of a box, or a written description of the box.

one hundred seven SMH 107

▲ Math Words and Ideas, p. 107

Math Words and Ideas

Changing the Dimensions and Changing the Volume

Company A and Company B both make identical boxes that have a volume of 6 cubes.

Original Box Design

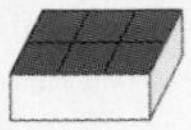

Dimensions: 3 × 2 × 1, holds 6 cubes

Each company has a plan to change the design of the box.

Company A plans to make a box that will hold twice as many cubes.

New Box Design: Company A

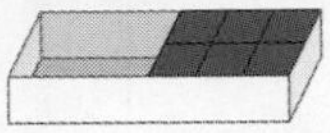

Dimensions: 6 × 2 × 1, holds 12 cubes

Company B plans to make a box with double the dimensions.

New Box Design: Company B

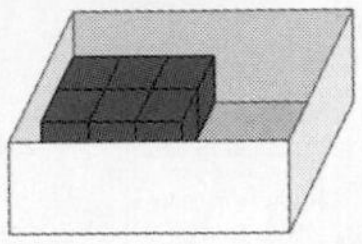

Dimensions: 6 × 4 × 2, holds 48 cubes

Four students discussed how the volume of each new box compares to the volume of the original box.

Company A

Alicia: *The volume of Company A's new box is twice the volume of the original box.*

Olivia: *Only one dimension changed. The 3 doubled to be a 6.*

Company B

Stuart: *Company B's new box will hold 8 times as many cubes as the original box.*

Tavon: *All three of the dimensions were multiplied by 2.*

Design a different box for Company A that will also hold twice as many cubes as the original 3 × 2 × 1 box.

Math Words and Ideas, p. 108

Math Words and Ideas

Standard Cubic Units

(page 1 of 2)

Math Words
- cubic centimeter
- cubic inch
- cubic foot
- cubic meter
- cubic yard

Volume is measured in cubic units.

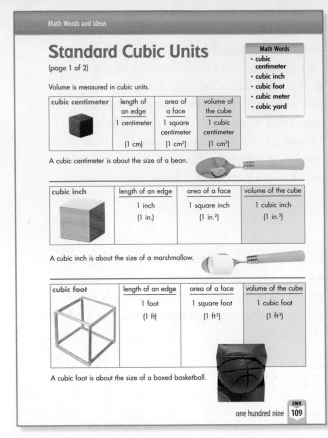

cubic centimeter	length of an edge	area of a face	volume of the cube
	1 centimeter (1 cm)	1 square centimeter (1 cm²)	1 cubic centimeter (1 cm³)

A cubic centimeter is about the size of a bean.

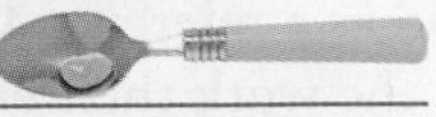

cubic inch	length of an edge	area of a face	volume of the cube
	1 inch (1 in.)	1 square inch (1 in.^{2})	1 cubic inch (1 in.^{3})

A cubic inch is about the size of a marshmallow.

cubic foot	length of an edge	area of a face	volume of the cube
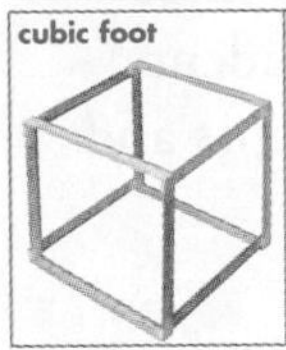	1 foot (1 ft)	1 square foot (1 ft^2)	1 cubic foot (1 ft^3)

A cubic foot is about the size of a boxed basketball.

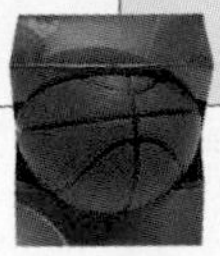

Math Words and Ideas, p. 109

Math Words and Ideas

Standard Cubic Units

(page 2 of 2)

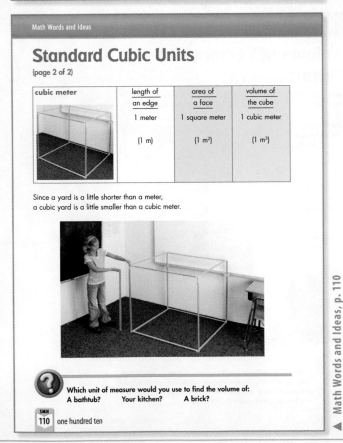

cubic meter	length of an edge	area of a face	volume of the cube
	1 meter (1 m)	1 square meter (1 m^2)	1 cubic meter (1 m^3)

Since a yard is a little shorter than a meter, a cubic yard is a little smaller than a cubic meter.

Which unit of measure would you use to find the volume of: A bathtub? Your kitchen? A brick?

Math Words and Ideas, p. 110

Math Words and Ideas

Geometric Solids

(page 1 of 4)

Math Words
- geometric solid

Here are some examples of geometric solids. These figures have three dimensions: length, width, and height.

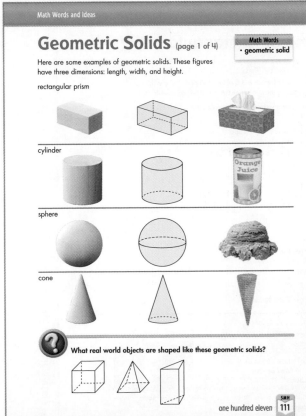

rectangular prism

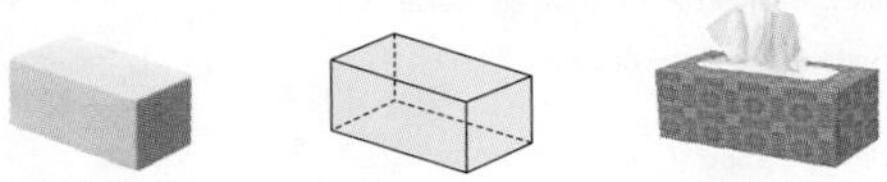

cylinder

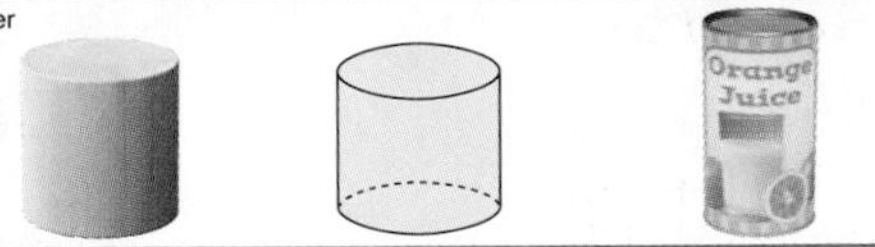

sphere

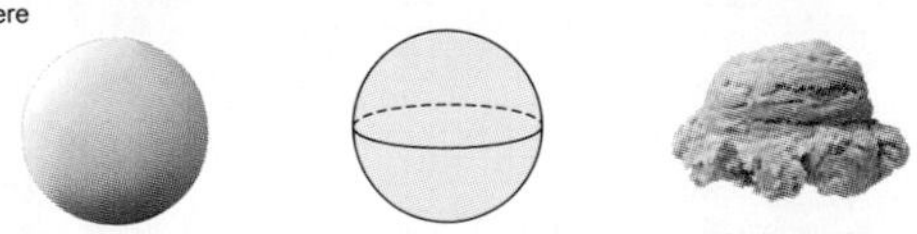

cone

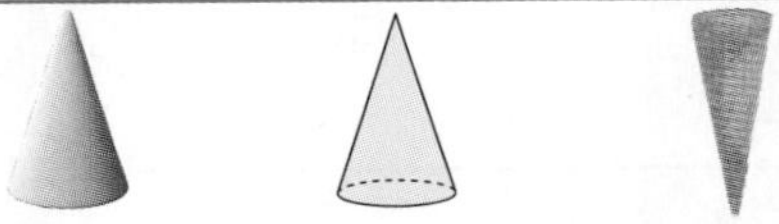

What real world objects are shaped like these geometric solids?

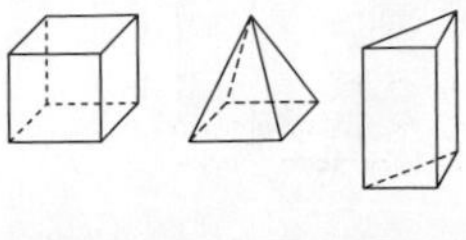

Math Words and Ideas, p. 111

Math Words and Ideas

Geometric Solids (page 2 of 4)

Math Words
- **face**
- **edge**
- **vertex**
- **vertices**

One way to describe a geometric solid is to identify the number of faces, edges, and vertices.

A face is a 2-D figure that makes up a flat surface of a 3-D solid.

An edge is a line segment where two faces meet.

A vertex is the point at a corner where edges meet.

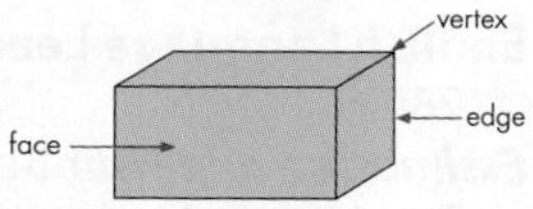

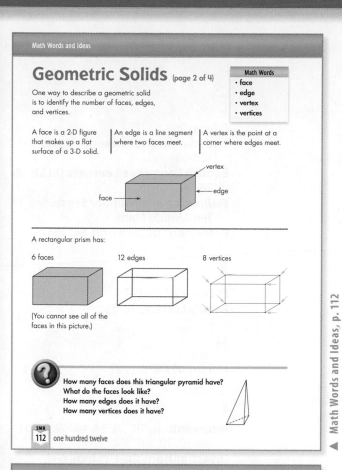

A rectangular prism has:

6 faces

12 edges

8 vertices

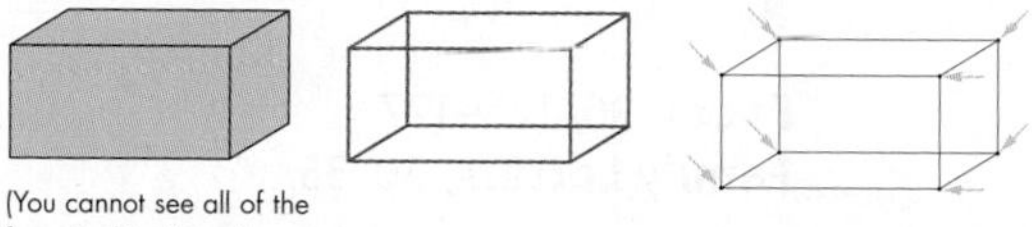

(You cannot see all of the faces in this picture.)

How many faces does this triangular pyramid have?
What do the faces look like?
How many edges does it have?
How many vertices does it have?

▲ Math Words and Ideas, p. 112

Math Words and Ideas

Geometric Solids (page 3 of 4)

Math Words
- **base**

All of these geometric solids are called prisms.

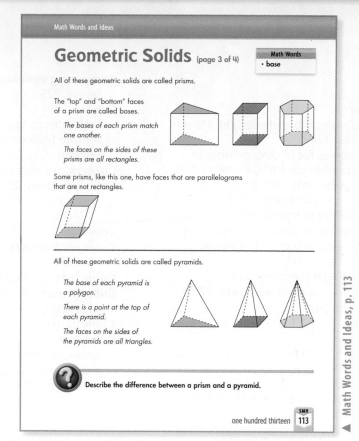

The "top" and "bottom" faces of a prism are called bases.

The bases of each prism match one another.

The faces on the sides of these prisms are all rectangles.

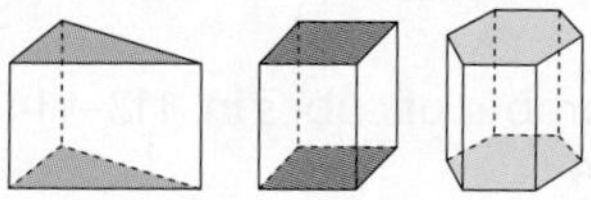

Some prisms, like this one, have faces that are parallelograms that are not rectangles.

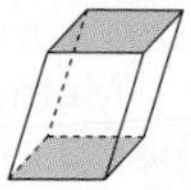

All of these geometric solids are called pyramids.

The base of each pyramid is a polygon.

There is a point at the top of each pyramid.

The faces on the sides of the pyramids are all triangles.

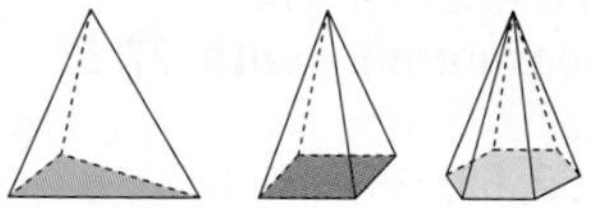

Describe the difference between a prism and a pyramid.

▲ Math Words and Ideas, p. 113

Math Words and Ideas

Geometric Solids (page 4 of 4)

The base of this rectangular prism measures 4 centimeters by 5 centimeters.

The height measures 8 centimeters.

The base of this rectangular pyramid measures 4 centimeters by 5 centimeters.

The height measures 8 centimeters.

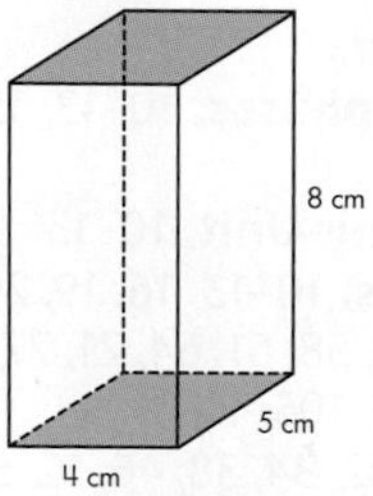

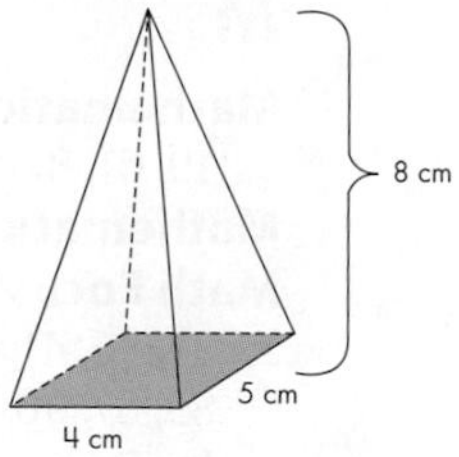

Note: The height of the pyramid is measured vertically from the base, not along the slope of the side.

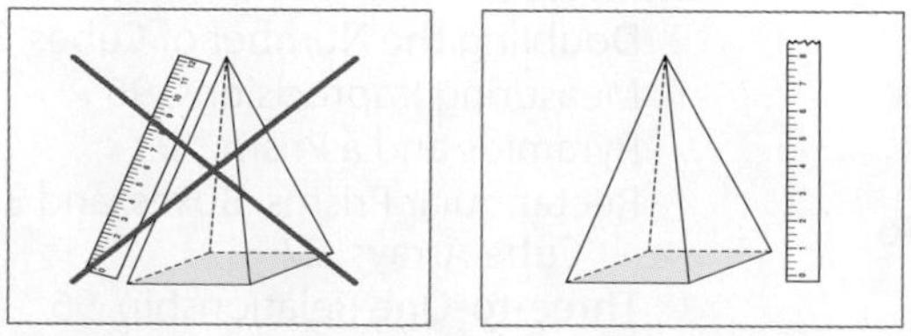

What is the volume of the rectangular prism above?
How do you think the volume of this rectangular pyramid compares to the volume of the rectangular prism above? How could you find out?

▲ Math Words and Ideas, p. 114

Index

IN THIS UNIT